D1417925

FOUNDATIONS OF THERMODYNAMICS

FOUNDATIONS OF
THERMODYNAMICS

PETER FONG

Professor of Physics
Utica College
Syracuse University

NEW YORK   OXFORD UNIVERSITY PRESS   1963

To Eugene P. Wigner

PREFACE

The logical structure of classical thermodynamics has often been criticized,* primarily on the ground that its foundations rest on a number of engineering concepts, such as the impossibility of the perpetual motion machine. While thermodynamics is essentially a macroscopic theory of equilibrium, it does not start from the exact laws of equilibrium; instead it is developed from principles that were proposed for a different purpose. As a result we can formulate only the sufficient condition of equilibrium but not the necessary condition. In other words, we do not know if a process of increasing entropy would actually take place spontaneously. Thus, the establishment of the law of increase of entropy from the second law is not a straightforward deduction; it requires an additional assumption. The difficulty manifests itself most clearly in the treatment of the chemical reactions, starting with Gibbs's paradox (see pp. 56–7). Furthermore, the entropy concept is first introduced as a purely mathematical quantity, and it becomes difficult later to give it statistical meaning. Besides, there are the endless discussions of the possible violation of the second law (e.g., by the Maxwell demon) which are irrelevant to the essence of thermodynamics.

* See, for example, P. W. Bridgman, *The Nature of Thermodynamics*, Harvard University Press, 1941; M. Born, *Natural Philosophy of Cause and Chance*, Oxford University Press, 1949.

The Carathéodory formulation avoids engineering concepts in introducing entropy, which is a major advantage; but it is still unable to deduce the necessary condition of equilibrium. In stating the basic physical principle, Carathéodory set forth a mathematical formulation of the physical fact that mechanical work can always be converted into heat but that the reverse is not always possible; yet the Carathéodory principle has nothing to say on the direction of heat flow in conduction, the experimental fact of which has to be invoked as a separate assumption to establish the law of increase of entropy. The abstruseness of the Carathéodory principle from a physical point of view and the lengthy detour into the mathematics of Pfaffian form also make it less attractive to physicists.

Since thermodynamics deals with macroscopic phenomena of equilibrium, it should be founded on the experimental facts concerning the macroscopic properties of equilibrium. The purpose of this book is to develop thermodynamics along this line. From the experimental facts it is possible to formulate a basic law for spontaneous processes which leads to the necessary and sufficient condition of equilibrium: the maximizing of a certain function of the thermodynamical variables. By using the macroscopic properties of equilibrium, it becomes possible to determine the explicit form of this function, which turns out to be the same as the entropy function in the conventional formulation. Thus, entropy may be introduced and the theoretical structure of thermodynamics may be established without the use of the cyclic heat engine. This formulation is established on a broader basis, including all spontaneous processes, not just the adiabatic processes considered in the Carathéodory formulation. It has the advantages but not the shortcomings of the Carathéodory formulation.

The first law of thermodynamics is assumed without change. The basic concepts of temperature and heat are defined and related to the basic laws (zeroth and first) in a similar manner as entropy is defined and related to the second law, to assure uniformity of viewpoint and treatment. No attempt is made to develop

vi

statistical thermodynamics except to point out the connection between the macroscopic theory and the microscopic theory; this can be established very naturally in the present approach.

This book is concerned primarily with the physical principles of thermodynamics. Mathematical deductions (thermodynamical relations and different forms of the equilibrium conditions) and detailed calculations will not be included here. Applications are discussed only for the purpose of illustrating physical principles; the chapter on applications is by no means intended to be a complete and balanced treatment. It is hoped that the discussions of physical principles may help to improve the understanding of thermodynamics. This book may be used as a supplementary text in thermodynamics courses for an exposition of the physical principles, leaving the mathematical elaborations and applications to be covered by other standard textbooks.

While this book was being prepared, Tisza† published his formulation of thermodynamics, which was the basis of a textbook by Callen.‡ Their starting point is similar to the one employed here, yet the development is very different. Tisza established the relation $dS = \delta Q/T$ in a special case, i.e., the case of constant volume and constant molar numbers. Needless to say, this relation should be established in general, and it should be established that only a change of δQ and nothing else may give rise to a change of entropy. In Tisza's treatment the intimate relation between this result and the reversible processes is not apparent. The identification of $(\partial U/\partial v)_{S,N}$ to pressure is not convincing: Since the physical meaning of constant S has not been specified yet at this stage we cannot interpret the meaning of $(\partial U/\partial v)_{S,N}$ in terms of U, v, and N only. In Callen's treatment the possibility of identifying $(\partial U/\partial v)_{S,N}$ to any function of pressure which also has the same value for two systems in mechanical equilibrium cannot be excluded. In the present formulation, the additive assumption used by Tisza is eliminated, at least for a large class of physical

† Annals of Physics, *13*, 1, (1961).
‡ *Thermodynamics*, John Wiley and Sons, Inc., New York, 1960.

systems, so that one does not have to bother about the physical meaning of the additive assumption as a basic postulate. Tisza treated the Gibbs thermodynamics and left the Clausius-Kelvin thermodynamics to Carathéodory. Here we treat thermodynamics as a whole. It may also be mentioned that Landau and Lifshitz[§] also treated thermodynamics from a starting point similar to Tisza's.

This book was first published in the spring of 1961. as a syllabus for student use. The author wishes to take this opportunity to thank Professor F. J. Belinfante of Purdue University and Professor Philip Morrison of Cornell for many stimulating discussions on the fundamental problems of thermodynamics, and also the staff of Oxford University Press for publishing the book for a wider audience.

Utica, New York   PETER FONG
December, 1962

[†] *Statistical Physics*, Addison-Wesley Publishing Company, Reading, Massachusetts, 1958.

CONTENTS

ϕ: the potential of
spontaneous
transition (for
thermal interaction).

ix

FOUNDATIONS OF THERMODYNAMICS

I

TEMPERATURE

THE ZEROTH LAW OF THERMODYNAMICS

Science is based on experience. We start the study of thermodynamics by a survey of our experience with heat phenomena.

The first thing we know of heat is the subjective sensation of hot and cold. Also, our sense organs can distinguish different degrees of hotness and coldness qualitatively. Furthermore, it is easy to establish that hot and cold are not absolute but relative; warm water may feel hot to a cold hand and cold to a warm hand. Therefore, an order may be established between any two objects: either A is warmer than B, $A > B$, or vice versa. It takes a large body of experience to establish that for a large number of material bodies A, B, C, . . . , the order between any two of them can be put together to form a one-dimensional sequence, such that when $A > B$, $B > C$ then it follows $A > C$, and that when $A = B$, $B = C$, it follows $A = C$. The statement that there exists such a one-dimensional sequence to describe the hot or cold property of material bodies is called the zeroth law of thermodynamics—a belated addition after the use of the terms "first law" and "second law" had become well established.* Like any other basic physical law, the zeroth law is the summary of a large body of experimental fact.

---

* The term "zeroth law" was suggested by R. H. Fowler. Its different formulations all serve the same purpose of establishing the physical concept "temperature."

3

The zeroth law may be represented mathematically by introducing a scalar quantity called temperature. Since the real number scale represents a one-dimensional continuous sequence, it can be made one-to-one related to the sequence of objects in the order of increasing warmness. The number so associated with the object is called the temperature T of the object. Hotter objects are represented by larger values of temperature; colder objects by smaller values. The fact that A is warmer than B is now represented by the mathematical inequality $T_A > T_B$. The introduction of the concept of temperature is thus a mathematical consequence of the zeroth law.

Although we have introduced the one-to-one correspondence, the exact relationship has not been specified. On the physical side we have introduced only a *sequence*; we have not introduced a *metric*. All mathematical representations that keep the order are equally legitimate. Therefore, the temperature scale is allowed a transformation that keeps the order invariant but changes the scale in any manner. We may construct many temperature scales differing not only in zero point and the size of the unit, such as the Centigrade scale and the Fahrenheit scale, but also in the calibration of the scale, such as the mercury scale and the alcohol scale.* All these scales are equally legitimate; no one is absolute. The so-called absolute temperature scale, to be introduced later, is actually a *universal* scale, in the sense that it is independent of the characteristics of the material employed in the thermometer. This scale may be more convenient than others, but convenience does not justify considering it to be absolute. The metric of the temperature scale is a redundant mathematical quantity having no physical significance in macroscopic theory. The one-degree difference in temperature near the freezing point of water and the one-degree difference near the boiling point cannot be equalized

* The mercury scale and the alcohol scale would be the same if the laws of expansion of mercury and alcohol were exactly the same. Actually, the linear law is only an approximation and no two materials behave exactly the same.

4

from a conceptual point of view because the two things cannot be brought together to compare.

Since temperature is a representation of a sequence, negative numbers may also be used as a mathematical extension of the positive number sequence. It is not surprising that negative temperatures on the absolute scale may be introduced as in the magnetic systems.

Zeroth Law never stated, not clearly indicated.

5

II

QUANTITY OF HEAT

THE FIRST LAW OF THERMODYNAMICS

Besides the existence of temperature, heat phenomena are characterized by the physical changes induced in objects of different temperature brought into contact (thermal interaction) with each other. For example, when a piece of ice is dropped into a volume of hot water the ice will melt. It does not take long to realize that the quantitative effect thus produced is not solely determined by the temperature of the hot object. Although a red-hot needle has a much higher temperature than a bath of hot water, the amount of ice it melts may be less than that melted by the bath of water. Obviously another quantity has come into play which determines the amount of ice melted. Our experience in this respect is summarized in the concept of the heat quantity, which determines the quantitative effect produced in thermal interaction. Incidentally, the quantity of heat is measured by the effect produced; one calorie is defined as the amount of heat that raises the temperature of one gram of water one degree Centigrade. The effect produced in an object is attributed to the introduction into the object of the heat quantity from the hot body. Thus two questions arise: What is the nature of the heat quantity? How does heat quantity transfer from one object to another?

The concept of heat quantity implies that the amount of heat concerned has a certain degree of permanence. The amount of heat necessary to raise one gram of water from zero degree to one degree Centigrade is always the same in spite of diurnal, seasonal, geographical changes, etc. Such a change of property as the increase of temperature by one degree is thus not likely due to the change of the function of the physical system but probably due to the introduction of a physical entity. In the "materialistic" eighteenth century, it was only natural to associate this entity with a *substance* which was called the caloric. Moreover, the experimental results concerning thermal interaction may be explained by considering the caloric as an indestructible, conserved quantity.

The caloric theory was replaced by the mechanical theory of heat in the nineteenth century. The experiments of Rumford and Davy and their arguments are common knowledge; the mechanical equivalent of heat was conclusively established by Joule (1840-65). Once this equivalence was established, the general principle of conservation of energy, including heat as a form of energy, followed logically, and is now known as the first law of thermodynamics. Historically, Robert Mayer in 1842 first originated the bold though speculative idea of a general principle of conservation of energy, which went beyond the framework of classical mechanics; but the precise mathematical formulation was achieved by Helmholtz in 1847. The important feature of the caloric theory—the concept of conservation—is retained in the new theory; only the range of application is enlarged to include mechanical interactions. Thermal and mechanical interactions are no longer considered to be independent phenomena; in fact the interplay of the two is the very subject to be investigated in thermodynamics.

Having dealt with the first question, we now come to the second: How does heat flow from one object into another? Heat always flows from an object of high temperature to an object of low temperature, and the flow will not stop until the temperatures become equal. This statement is the summary of a large body of experimental facts concerning the flow of heat. This problem is a special case of a more general problem which is to be discussed in

7

the next chapter. A general principle (the second law of thermo-dynamics) governing such processes as the heat flow will be introduced there.

The three aspects of heat phenomena discussed so far cannot be separated from each other. Experimentally, the hot or cold sensation cannot be ascertained without thermal interaction with the hand or the thermometer. An amount of heat is involved which passes from one object to another. Therefore, temperature cannot be defined independently of the heat quantity and the law of heat flow. Nevertheless, the separation of the three aspects is typical of the analytical approach in science; and conditions may be provided experimentally such that only one aspect stands out. This aspect may then be investigated experimentally without having to consider the complication caused by including the other two. The thermal interaction may take place between two objects, one having a very small heat capacity so that the amount of heat transfer involved is negligibly small. This is the basis of *thermometry*, which is concerned with the measurement of temperature; the small object is the thermometer. On the other hand, one object may be maintained at constant temperature by its large mass or by the use of latent heat, so that heat quantity may be measured without the involvement of a change of temperature. On this basis, we can establish the concepts of temperature and heat quantity, perform measurements of them, and establish the basic laws of the heat phenomena.

By introducing the temperature concept we assign to any material object* a property which determines its thermal interactions with other objects. The mechanical properties of a material object are specified by a number of mechanical quantities such as the pressure of a gas and the gravitational energy of a weight (these may be generalized to electric and magnetic quantities). Since thermal interaction and mechanical interaction are

---

* A temperature may also be assigned to the blackbody radiation field, which is not a material object. In general, any thermodynamic system has a temperature.

8

related (the first law) and are treated together in thermodynamics, we have to specify all these quantities for a complete description of the thermal and mechanical properties of a material object. For a mixture of materials, we must also specify the composition. When we consider an isolated material object or system from the point of view of its thermal, mechanical, and composition properties, it is considered as a *thermodynamic system*. A thermodynamic system, by definition, is isolated until interactions with other systems are specified. The quantities specifying the thermal, mechanical, and composition properties are called *thermodynamic variables*. Among the mechanical variables, some are dependent on the thermal and compositional variables, such as the pressure of a mixture of reacting gases, and some are not, such as the gravitational energy of a weight. We limit the term *thermodynamic variables* to exclude the latter kind, which are called *purely mechanical variables*. For a given thermodynamic system there exist a number of *independent thermodynamic variables* which determine the thermodynamic properties of the system completely. A thermodynamic system with its thermodynamic properties completely specified by a set of independent thermodynamic variables is said to be in a specified *thermodynamic state*. When a system changes from one thermodynamic state to another it is said to have undergone a *thermodynamic process*. Since we have separated the purely mechanical variables from the thermodynamic variables, a change of the gravitational energy alone, for example, does not change the thermodynamic state of the system. The justification for this assertion is that the thermal processes such as heat flow and, more generally, the spontaneous processes to be introduced in the second law, which are our main concern, are independent of the purely mechanical variables, which are therefore not considered.

We shall explain the concepts introduced above by examples. The simplest kind of thermodynamic system is a gas. A definite amount of gas, sealed inside a heat-insulated cylinder, provided with an air-tight, frictionless, heat-insulated piston locked at a

9

fixed position, is a thermodynamic system. It is isolated with respect to the transfer of heat, work, and matter. It may be made to interact with other thermodynamic systems brought into contact with it by (1) making the wall of the cylinder heat-conducting so that transfer of heat may take place, (2) releasing the lock of the piston so that transfer of work may take place, (3) making the wall of the cylinder permeable or semipermeable so that transfer of matter may take place, and (4) combining any or all of these three procedures. The first three types of interactions are determined respectively by the temperature, the pressure, and the molar numbers specifying the composition of the gas. These quantities are considered to be thermodynamic variables. These variables can be varied independently. On the other hand, an equal number of functions of these variables may be constructed and used as a new set of independent thermodynamic variables. For example, the volume of the gas is a function of its temperature, pressure, and molar numbers. It may be used as a thermodynamic variable but is not an independent one if temperature, pressure, and molar numbers are used as the independent thermodynamic variables.

A thermodynamic system is not necessarily three-dimensional. As long as a system can exchange heat and work with other systems it is a thermodynamic system. A surface under tension— for instance, a sheet of stretched rubber or the surface of a liquid with a large surface tension—can do work as well as absorb heat; it is a thermodynamic system, but a two-dimensional one. The mechanical variable corresponding to pressure P is in this case the surface tension T. The variable corresponding to volume V is the surface area A. The work done by a gas in an infinitesimal thermodynamic process is $P\,dV$ whereas that by the surface is $-T\,dA$. The minus sign is introduced because tension is a negative pressure.

One-dimensional thermodynamic systems also exist. Examples are the stretched metal wire and the rubber band. The mechanical variable is the tension of the wire T and the variable corresponding

10

to the volume is the length of the wire L. The work done in an infinitesimal process is $-T\,dL$.

Since the effect of mechanical interaction is the exchange of work, any interaction causing an exchange of work may be considered mechanical in thermodynamics. Thus electrical interaction is considered mechanical. An electric cell, which can perform work by drawing a current and can absorb work by forcing a current through it in the opposite direction, may be considered a thermodynamic system; it is not a purely mechanical system, because in charging or discharging there is also a thermal effect, i.e., heat is absorbed or released. The theory of the electric cell is thus a thermodynamic problem, not merely an electric problem. Since in thermodynamics we are interested only in the interplay of thermal and mechanical properties of a system (essentially the exchange of heat and work) we do not care how the electrical current is produced. This pertains to the microscopic theory. In the macroscopic theory our attitude is to take the mechanical and thermal properties of a system for granted and proceed to investigate the relations between them. For the cell the mechanical variable corresponding to pressure is the electromotive force E. The variable corresponding to volume is the amount of charge Q passing through the circuit during discharge. The work done in an infinitesimal process is $E\,dQ$. The composition of the chemicals of the cell, i.e., the molar numbers of the reactants and the products, are no longer independent variables. They now depend on Q.

In a similar manner a thermal couple may be considered as a thermodynamic system; there is a mechanical effect accompanied by a thermal effect. On the other hand, an A.C. generator is a purely mechanical system, not a thermodynamic one.

The inclusion of the composition of a system in the thermodynamic variables may be exemplified by the case of a mixture of reacting gases, e.g., N_2, H_2, and NH_3. The mixture has all the thermodynamic properties of a gas plus the property of being able to change the relative composition through a reversible chemical

11

reaction. Since any chemical reaction involves the absorption or release of heat and work, the reacting gases form a thermodynamic system. The change of composition is related to the thermal and mechanical effects; thus thermodynamics is closely related to the theory of chemical reactions. In thermodynamics we are not interested in knowing how N_2 and H_2 combine to form NH_3. This question is the concern of atomic physics. Once nitrogen and hydrogen are known to combine to form ammonia, we are interested in discovering the relations between the chemical, thermal and mechanical changes. We do not even care if nitrogen and hydrogen are made of molecules and molecules are made of atoms. In a sense a thermodynamic system is a black box specified by nothing but a set of properties concerning the absorption of heat, the performance of work, and the change of composition.

In thermodynamics we discuss the thermal, mechanical, and composition properties of a system together only because they are related to one another. This justifies our exclusion of the purely mechanical variables from the thermodynamic variables because they are independent of the others. A metal wire may be charged electrically and placed in an electric field. The additional mechanical property gained does not affect the thermodynamic properties of the wire (such as the temperature coefficient of the Young's modulus), which are our main concern. Thus the charge is not a thermodynamic variable. The same applies to the gravitational energy of a weight.

The concept of the thermodynamic system may be generalized beyond material systems. The blackbody radiation field inside an enclosure is a thermodynamic system because it has thermal and mechanical properties similar to other systems, just as a gas does. It has a temperature. It can absorb or release heat and work. The mechanical variable is the radiation pressure. As long as a system can exchange heat and work with other systems it is a thermodynamic system. Not even matter is required.

In thermal interaction both systems undergo thermodynamic

processes until their temperatures finally become equal. Then the thermodynamic state of either system changes no more and the two systems are said to be in *thermal equilibrium*. Any thermodynamic system may be considered as being made up of two or more interacting subdivisions. If these subdivisions were not in equilibrium at the beginning, they would have reached equilibrium by themselves after some time. Therefore, we imply by the term thermodynamic system that the different parts of the system are in equilibrium; in particular, the temperature is everywhere the same.

The zeroth law enables us to assign a quantity temperature to any object. In a similar manner the first law of thermodynamics enables us to assign another quantity to any object, that is, the *internal energy*. Consider a change of thermodynamic state of a system from state 1 to state 2. The heat taken into the system accompanying this change is designated by ΔQ; the mechanical work performed by the system ΔW. According to the general law of conservation of energy, the difference $\Delta Q - \Delta W$ must be balanced by another form of energy; thus we assume that the material system possesses an amount of energy, i.e., the internal energy U which may be changed from state 1 to state 2 by an amount ΔU such that $\Delta U = \Delta Q - \Delta W$. The sum of all kinds of energy is thus conserved. Now, let a system go through a series of changes of state and finally return to its initial state. The total amount of heat absorbed $\oint dQ$ must equal the total amount of work performed $\oint dW$; otherwise, by repeating the cycle indefinitely we can create or destroy any amount of energy as we wish, which is against the conservation law. Consequently, the integral of dU over the cycle $\oint dU$ must be zero. This means that the internal energy U is dependent only on the thermodynamic state, independent of the previous history of the system. In other words, U is a function of the thermodynamic variables, independent of the path by which the state is reached. The same may be stated by saying that ΔU (which is defined by $\Delta Q - \Delta W$) is an exact differential.

13

Since internal energy is a function of the thermodynamic variables, and any set of independent variables is equally legitimate, we can always perform a transformation of the independent variables so that one of the new independent variables is the internal energy and thus use internal energy as a thermodynamic variable.

III

THE LAW OF SPONTANEOUS PROCESSES
THE SECOND LAW OF THERMODYNAMICS

In the preceding chapter we mentioned the fact that heat always flows from a hot object into a cold object in thermal interaction. In this process the two interacting systems undergo a series of changes of thermodynamic states until they reach an equilibrium. We considered this process as the third aspect of the heat phenomena. Actually because thermal, mechanical, and composition properties are related to one another this process is a special case of a more general process: Two thermodynamic systems with different thermal, mechanical, composition properties may interact not only thermally to change their thermal properties but also mechanically to change their mechanical properties and also by diffusion to change their composition, or two or three types of interaction may take place simultaneously. In all cases the two interacting systems undergo a series of changes of their thermodynamic states and eventually equilibrium is established, that is, their thermodynamic states change no more. These thermodynamic processes are called *spontaneous processes* because they proceed automatically without any external influence once the two systems are allowed to interact. The purpose of this chapter is to study the basic law of spontaneous processes,*

---

* To confine the second law, and thus thermodynamics as a whole, to the discussion of spontaneous processes of thermal, mechanical, and composition of which the process of thermal interaction is a special case.

Once we have the basic law of spontaneous processes, the condition for the establishment of an equilibrium may be deduced. It is through this condition that thermodynamics is related to the study of the properties of matter. Since most macroscopic systems are in equilibrium internally among their constituent parts or externally with the surroundings, the equilibrium condition is the key to the study of many properties of material systems. For example, the phenomenon of change of boiling point by increasing pressure is actually the manifestation of the change of equilibrium pressure between a liquid and its vapor due to a change of temperature. The solution of the problem lies in the determination of the equilibrium condition with temperature as a parameter. In chemical reactions the reactants and the products usually reach an equilibrium. By using the equilibrium condition we may deduce the law of mass action. A further example may be found in the problem of heat radiation. Although radiation is not an equilibrium process, its basic law (Stefan-Boltzmann Law) may be deduced by considering the equilibrium between a radiating body and a radiation field.

As stated before, most properties of matter are equilibrium properties. If a system starts with a state not in equilibrium, it will reach equilibrium by its own accord, usually within a very short period of time. The time required for a gas to reach equilibrium is as small as 10^{-9} sec.; most gases we deal with are already in equilibrium. On the other hand there are problems concerning nonequilibrium processes for which *thermodynamics of irreversible*

---

changes may seem a rather limited approach. Actually it covers all essential parts of thermodynamics as a theory of equilibrium. Furthermore this approach is the exact macroscopic counterpart of statistical mechanics (microscopic theory of equilibrium) in which we consider isolated systems (microcanonical ensembles), systems in thermal equilibrium (canonical ensembles), systems in composition equilibrium (grand canonical ensembles) and systems in mechanical equilibrium (generalized ensembles); see, for example, Terrell L. Hill, *Statistical Mechanics*, McGraw-Hill Book Company, 1956, Chapters 1 and 2, particularly p. 48.

processes has been developed recently. In this book we shall be concerned only with the equilibrium problems.

The conventional second law of thermodynamics was introduced by Clausius (1850) and Kelvin (1851) independently. The concept of absolute temperature was originated by Kelvin. The concept of entropy was introduced by Clausius (1865), who also summarized the two thermodynamical laws by saying that the total energy of the universe is a constant and the total entropy of the universe always increases. The historical starting point of thermodynamics was an engineering problem of converting heat into mechanical work. In this respect Carnot (1824) had actually discovered the essence of the second law decades before it was stated, but his theory was based on the now obsolete caloric theory. It must be borne in mind that before 1850 the caloric theory was still a reputable theory despite the experiments of Rumford and Davy. The success of the Carnot theory and the conflict between the caloric theory and the mechanical theory of heat were reconciled in the 1850's when physicists recognized that there should be two independent laws in thermodynamics—the First and the Second—not just one, the Carnot principle based on the caloric theory.

When thermodynamics was later applied to a wide range of problems in physics and chemistry, we still used its basic concept (conversion of heat to work) and its mathematical apparatus (entropy) that originated in engineering. The engineering elements seem to be irrelevant to the physical and chemical problems of interest (see pp. 56–57). Thus we are faced with a situation which Bridgman described as a river rising higher than its source. Obviously the only way to avoid the difficulties involved in forcing a river to rise higher than its source is to put the source of the river at the highest point; then the river flows all by itself. This has never been done. In the latter part of the nineteenth century, many attempts were made to explain the second law in terms of mechanics; none were successful. Finally, the thermodynamic laws found a statistical interpretation in the microscopic theory by

17

Boltzmann, which gave rise to a new branch of physics—*statistical thermodynamics*.

Although the physical problem is thus solved in microscopic theory, the logical structure of *classical thermodynamics* as a macroscopic theory remains in an unsatisfactory state. It has been neglected probably in the belief that no new physical discovery of fundamental importance is to be expected. Carathéodory (1909) was the first to try to establish thermodynamics without the engineering concepts, but he stopped halfway. According to the previous discussion, thermodynamics must be formulated as a theory of equilibrium to begin with; the engineering applications should come out of it as a deduction. Therefore we start our discussion of the second law by establishing the law of spontaneous processes.

It is natural that the development of science is occasioned by accidents, and scientific breakthroughs are initiated more by insight than by reasoning. The historical order is usually not the logical order. However, once the whole picture is in sight, there is no excuse for not having the logical order straightened out.

1. Survey of experimental facts

We begin by surveying the experimental facts of spontaneous processes. These form the basis on which we may establish a law governing such processes.

We limit ourselves to the interactions between two systems, each of which is already in equilibrium within itself; an example is the exchange of heat between a hot gas and a cold gas when brought into thermal contact. Two interacting systems are said to form a *composite system*. This is a limited program. However, the results obtained may be easily generalized to the interactions of more than two systems. Actually a general nonequilibrium system such as the atmosphere of the Earth may be subdivided into a number of interacting systems; each may be considered to be in equilibrium by itself. Thus we may speak of the temperature and pressure of a particular city in spite of the fact that temperature and pressure are not in equilibrium in the whole atmosphere. The spontaneous processes of such a system may be analyzed in terms of the law of spontaneous processes for two interacting systems.

For convenience we consider two gases as examples of two thermodynamic systems. The conclusion derived is applicable to other thermodynamic systems. The thermodynamic state of a *given amount* of gas may be changed, for example, by changing its pressure P. Once P is fixed the state may still be changed by changing its volume V. Once P and V are fixed we have no way of changing it further by imparting heat and performing work. The other thermodynamic properties of the gas, such as the temperature T, are completely determined by P and V. These are experimental facts. The functional relation between P, V, and T is called the *equation of state* of the gas. Thus there are only two independent variables, which may be P, V or P, T or T, V. In each representation the other variable T or V or P, respectively, is a dependent variable and the functional dependence is specified by the equation of state.

We now consider two gases in the states (P_1, V_1) and (P_2, V_2), respectively. If the two gases are completely isolated from each other nothing will happen to them, both being already in equilibrium by themselves. Changes of thermodynamic states of the two gases will take place when the two gases are allowed to interact. Since a thermodynamic state is characterized by the thermal, mechanical, and composition properties of a system, we can distinguish three types of interaction which are related to each of the three properties, respectively.

(1) *Thermal interaction.* This is defined as the interaction which allows the two gases to exchange heat. The physical condition allowing it to take place is that the two gases be separated by a heat-conducting wall. If the wall has a large heat capacity, it becomes a third party of the interaction; it takes up some heat in itself. To concentrate our attention on interaction between two systems, we assume the wall to be infinitely thin so

19

that its heat capacity is vanishingly small. It follows that the increase of heat of the first system dQ_1 equals the negative of the increase of heat of the second system dQ_2.

$$dQ_1 = -dQ_2. \tag{1}$$

We shall always assume the availability of such a wall in all thermal interactions.

The experimental facts concerning thermal interactions may be summarized in the following statement: heat always flows from the gas of high temperature to the gas of low temperature until the two gases reach the same temperature. From the viewpoint of thermodynamic processes we may state it alternately. The two gases undergo a series of changes of their thermodynamic states until an equilibrium state is reached that is characterized by the equality of the temperature. Since thermodynamic states are defined for equilibrium states, the above statement has the following meaning: after the conducting wall is introduced at a time t_0 it may be removed later at times t_1, t_2, ... The thermodynamic states of the two gases at t_1, t_2, . . . , are different from those at t_0, and the series of states converge to the final equilibrium state. We notice that this particular type of interaction leads to a particular type of equilibrium specified by a particular condition. We say that *thermal interaction* leads to *thermal equilibrium* specified by the *equilibrium condition* that the temperatures of the two gases be equal. The *independent variable of the interaction* is the amount of heat transferred dQ_1 (or dQ_2). Other variable quantities not allowed to change in the processes are said to be *constrained*.

(2) *Mechanical interaction.* This is defined as the interaction which allows the two gases to exchange mechanical work. The physical condition allowing it to take place is that the two gases be separated by a moveable, frictionless, heat-insulated and air-tight piston. Again, to avoid letting the piston become a third party of the interaction, it is assumed to have an infinitely large compressibility so that the piston as a thermodynamic system does not

20

absorb work ($P \, dV$). The work performed by the first gas dW_1 is $P_1 \, dV_1$; that of the second gas dW_2 is $P_2 \, dW_2$. Although

$$dV_1 = -dV_2, \qquad \textit{is this necessarily true? Why?} \qquad (2)$$

P_1 and P_2 may not be the same. Thus $dW_1 + dW_2$ is not zero; actually this sum equals the kinetic energy of the piston. The piston will vibrate back and forth with a period determined by its mass. If no mechanism is provided to dissipate this amount of kinetic energy the system will not reach equilibrium; it keeps on vibrating. Actually, even though we assume the piston is frictionless with the wall, the system will eventually come to an equilibrium because the kinetic energy will be dissipated by the viscosity of the gases. When equilibrium is established we find that the pressures of the two gases are equal. (We required the frictionless assumption to assure equality of pressure in equilibrium.) The experimental facts concerning mechanical interactions may be summarized by saying that *mechanical interaction* leads to *mechanical equilibrium* specified by the equilibrium condition that the pressures of the two gases be equal. The independent variable of the interaction is the change of volume dV_1 (or dV_2). Other variables such as dQ are constrained.

(3) *Diffusive interaction.* This is defined as the interaction which allows the two gases to exchange their material. Here it is tacitly assumed that the two gases are distinct, such as oxygen and hydrogen. The physical condition allowing it to take place is that the two gases be separated by a permeable membrane. The membrane may be permeable to one gas but not to the other (semipermeable membrane); it may also be permeable to both. Permeable membranes and semipermeable membranes do exist in nature, but whether a membrane permeable only to a particular gas exists in nature or not is irrelevant. The existence of some semipermeable membranes shows the feasibility of such a membrane. Therefore, a membrane permeable only to a particular gas can always be conceived mentally if only for the sake of argument (just as a spaceship able to travel half as fast as light may be

21

rightfully conceived in spite of the fact that it can never be developed on the Earth; on the other hand, a spaceship that travels twice as fast as light cannot be rightfully conceived because it is against the law of nature). Consider for simplicity that only one gas is allowed to diffuse. The change of mass of gas 1 due to this diffusion may be denoted by dm_1; that of gas 2, dm_2. The membrane is not assumed to absorb any gas and therefore

$$dm_1 = -dm_2. \tag{3}$$

Diffusive interactions eventually lead to *diffusive equilibrium* specified by the equilibrium condition that the density of each species of the diffusing gases becomes uniform subject to the restriction of the existing constraints. The independent variable of the interaction is the change of mass dm_1 (or dm_2) of the gas allowed to diffuse.

In some cases, two or three types of interaction may take place simultaneously. In many chemical reactions dQ, dV, and dm are all allowed to vary. The flow of heat will not come to a stop until thermal equilibrium is established. The change of volume will not come to a stop until mechanical equilibrium is established. The change of concentration will not come to a stop until diffusive equilibrium is established. Thus, the *chemical equilibrium* of these reactions implies the concurrence of all three types of equilibrium. As a result, the theory of equilibrium to be developed here is directly applicable to chemical reactions.

2. The law of spontaneous processes

The spontaneous processes due to the three types of interaction exhibit one common feature which is characteristic of thermo-dynamic systems. The change of the thermodynamic state of either system during the interaction proceeds in one specified direction. In other words, once a system has passed a particular thermo-dynamic state, this state will never be reached again in the same process; furthermore, the succession of states the process passes converge to the equilibrium state as a limit. The thermodynamic variables are usually monotonically increasing or decreasing as interaction proceeds.* This situation is different from that of purely mechanical systems (in particular, bound systems) in which the motion of a particle or a rigid body has a certain periodicity so that after a definite period of time the system returns to where it started. In each spontaneous process, some thermodynamic variables of the two systems change monotonically; therefore, we can construct a function of these variables in such a way that the function *increases* monotonically as the interaction proceeds and reaches a maximum at equilibrium. For example, in the thermal interaction the temperature T_1 of the hot gas decreases monotonically; the temperature T_2 of the cold gas increases monotonically. Thus, we can construct a function f of T_1 and T_2, for example, $f(T_1, T_2) \doteq -|T_1 - T_2|$, which increases monotonically and reaches the maximum value zero when equilibrium is established. Furthermore, there exist infinitely many functions having this property; in fact any monotonically increasing function g of $-|T_1 - T_2|$ has the same property. Thus $f(T_1, T_2) = g(-|T_1 - T_2|)$. Such functions may be used as indicators to show in which direction the process proceeds. When we are given two neighboring states of the composite system in thermal interaction specified by the temperature (t_1, t_2) and (t_1', t_2') we may evaluate the function $f(T_1, T_2)$ for the two states; if $f(t_1', t_2')$ is greater than $f(t_1, t_2)$ then we may conclude that the state (t_1, t_2) will change itself into the other (t_1', t_2'). Of course the same purpose may be achieved by constructing monotonically *decreasing* functions of T_1 and T_2, which may be obtained by just adding a minus sign. Since the two alternatives are equivalent, we choose the monotonically increasing function to conform with conventional usage. Such a function

---

* The example of mechanical interaction discussed before is somewhat different. The thermodynamic variables change in time according to a damped oscillatory curve. When the frequency is high (mass of piston small) the physically significant quantity is the average value over several oscillations, which changes monotonically as interaction proceeds.

23

may be called the *potential of spontaneous transition for thermal interaction* and may be denoted by ϕ_t. The use of the term *potential* arises from the analogy with gravitational potential. A body falls from a point of high gravitational potential to another of low potential; the value of the potential thus determines in which direction the body falls. In a similar manner we may construct a *potential of spontaneous transition for mechanical interaction* ϕ_m which is a function of certain thermodynamic variables of the two interacting systems. As the interaction proceeds ϕ_m increases. Likewise there are infinitely many ways of constructing such a function. Since ϕ_t and ϕ_m are constructed independently they are not expected to be the same. However, out of the infinitely many choices of each of them, the possibility of finding a common one cannot be excluded. Similarly we may construct a *potential of spontaneous transition for diffusive interaction* ϕ_d and the same discussion above applies.

Up to this point we have only given a description; we have not yet introduced a physical principle. By comparing the three types of interaction a physical principle emerges. The similarity of the three types of interaction seems to indicate that the existence of the potentials of spontaneous transition may have a physical significance besides being just a mathematical convenience. It may well be that the interacting thermodynamic systems possess a physical property which, because of a physical mechanism not yet made clear in macroscopic theory, tends to increase in *all* spontaneous processes and reaches a maximum in equilibrium.* In the special case of thermal interaction, this physical property manifests itself as ϕ_t; in mechanical interaction as ϕ_m; in diffusive interaction as ϕ_d. Mathematically our conjecture is equivalent to saying that a common function ϕ may be found among the various choices of ϕ_t, ϕ_m, and ϕ_d. The assumption for the existence of such a physical property is based on a generalization of the experimental facts which are analyzed and compared in the above

---

* The nature of this property and mechanism is to be discussed in statistical mechanics in a later chapter. This can be done only in a microscopic theory.

discussion; the validity of this generalization is to be tested by comparing the deductions from this assumption with experimental results. In a general spontaneous process where several types of interaction may take place simultaneously, the function ϕ also always increases because it increases for each individual interaction. Accordingly, we call ϕ the *potential of spontaneous transition*. This assumption is taken to be our basic law of spontaneous processes and may be stated as follows:

> For two interacting thermodynamic systems specified by thermodynamic variables (P_1, V_1), (P_2, V_2), respectively,* there exists a physical property of the composite system represented by a function of the thermodynamic variables $\phi(P_1, V_1, P_2, V_2)$ such that a spontaneous process always takes place to change a state of the composite system with a low value of ϕ to a neighboring state with a high value of ϕ, which is accessible from the first state by the interactions.

Since the thermodynamic properties of a thermodynamic system are completely determined by its thermodynamic variables, the properties of two interacting systems are completely determined by the variables of both. Therefore if a potential of spontaneous transition ϕ does exist, it must be a function of P_1, V_1, P_2, and V_2 exclusively.† The quantity ϕ represents a collective property of the two systems, but we have not yet specified how the properties of the two systems are to be put together to give rise to such a collective property.

In the special case of thermal interaction, dQ is allowed to vary.

---

* We omit all other thermodynamic variables except P and V for simplicity. The result may be easily generalized when the other variables are included.
† The purely mechanical variables are not related to any spontaneous processes that reach equilibrium. The processes that concern us are independent of the purely mechanical variables. Therefore ϕ is independent of them. This justifies our excluding the purely mechanical variables from the thermodynamic variables. Example: If the surface tension of a liquid is independent of any thermal effects, it is a purely mechanical variable and therefore the surface area is not a thermodynamic variable. The thermal, mechanical, and diffusive interactions of the liquid with other systems are independent of the shape (and thus the surface area) of the liquid.

By varying the value of dQ, we generate a series of thermodynamic states of the composite system accessible by the interaction. Each of them is associated with a value of ϕ. According to our basic assumption, the composite system in a state with a low value of ϕ will always change itself into a neighboring state of a high value of ϕ among the accessible states. Therefore a state cannot be in equilibrium if there are neighboring states in the series with higher values of ϕ. As a result a necessary condition of equilibrium is that ϕ be a maximum. This condition is also sufficient since once ϕ reaches a maximum no further change is possible. Thus the necessary and sufficient condition of equilibrium is that ϕ be a maximum with respect to dQ.

Likewise the necessary and sufficient condition of equilibrium in mechanical interaction is that ϕ be a maximum with respect to dV; that of diffusive equilibrium is that ϕ be a maximum with respect to dm.

When a number of interactions take place simultaneously, dQ, dV, and dm are allowed to vary at the same time. The variation of these variables leads to the generation of a set of thermodynamic states of the composite system accessible by the interactions. Each corresponds to a value of ϕ. Our basic assumption requires that a state with a low value of ϕ will always change itself into a neighboring state with a high value of ϕ among the set of accessible states. Likewise we establish the necessary and sufficient condition of equilibrium: *The value of ϕ for the equilibrium state is a maximum with respect to the variations of dQ, dV, and dm consistent with the constraints of the system.* This is the general condition of thermodynamic equilibrium.

The equilibrium condition follows directly from our basic assumption. Incidentally, the basic assumption allows us to formulate the *necessary* conditions which cannot be formulated without additional assumption in the traditional formulation based on the law of heat engine (or in the Carathéodory formulation). In the practical applications of the equilibrium condition we must have the exact specification of the constraints. In most cases

26

this can be done. In the exceptional cases where we are not certain about the constraints we still cannot predict which state of equilibrium the system will finally reach (e.g., para-hydrogen or ortho-hydrogen). However, the problem has become one of tracking down the constraints instead of one involving fundamental principles of thermodynamics.

We have mentioned that the function ϕ reduces to ϕ_t, ϕ_m, and ϕ_d as special cases. We now consider the reverse. If a function ψ is found which reduces to ϕ_t, ϕ_m, and ϕ_d in special cases, then we can show that ψ may be used as ϕ. Consider a general spontaneous process in which dQ, dV, and dm are allowed to vary. The necessary and sufficient condition for this process to reach equilibrium is the concurrence of thermal, mechanical, and diffusive equilibrium. The necessary and sufficient condition of these equilibriums is that ψ (which reduces to ϕ_t, ϕ_m, and ϕ_d) be a maximum with respect to the variations of dQ, dV, and dm. Thus ψ serves the purpose of ϕ. As a result, to find a ϕ it is *sufficient* to determine a function which reduces to ϕ_t, ϕ_m, and ϕ_d in the three special cases. Inasmuch as there are infinitely many ways of constructing ϕ_t, ϕ_m, and ϕ_d, respectively, it is possible that a common one may be found.

Once a function ϕ is found we may construct infinitely many other functions for the potential of spontaneous transition because any monotonically increasing function of ϕ will serve the same purpose. Among the infinitely many possible choices there is a *possibility* that one exists having the following property:

$$\phi(P_1, V_1, P_2, V_2) = \phi_1(P_1, V_1) + \phi_2(P_2, V_2). \qquad (4)$$

In other words, this ϕ is to be an additive quantity with respect to the two systems. In the following section we shall show that such a function does exist. Once its existence is established, we choose to develop our theory on the basis of such a ϕ function. This is not an additional assumption; this is a choice we are entitled to because all possible forms of ϕ are equally legitimate. (We may also choose to work with a multiplicative function ϕ and develop an equally useful theory if this choice proves to be feasible and more convenient.) One reason for such a choice is the analogy with gravitational potential which is also additive.

3. Determination of the explicit form of ϕ

A. THE REVERSIBLE PROCESS

We proceed to determine the functional dependence of ϕ on the thermodynamic variables and to show that an additive ϕ does exist at the same time. First we assume the additivity from which we can determine the functional form of ϕ to within an additive constant by a series of considerations of the equilibrium properties. We next verify that the function so determined does possess the property required of ϕ_t, ϕ_m, and ϕ_d and therefore, according to a previous discussion, it qualifies as the potential of spontaneous transition. The verification is necessary to establish the existence of the additive function of ϕ. From now on when we speak of the potential of spontaneous transition, we may refer to *a single* thermodynamic system, e.g., $\phi_1(P_1, V_1)$ or $\phi_2(P_2, V_2)$ (instead of the composite system) from which the potential of spontaneous transition of the composite system may be obtained by addition.

For the purpose of determining the explicit form of $\phi(P, V)$ of a single thermodynamic system we introduce an idealized process— the *reversible process*—which is defined as follows:

> A reversible process is an idealized spontaneous process taking place in a composite system such that the value $\phi(P_1, V_1, P_2, V_2)$ of the composite system remains constant as the independent variable of the process dQ, dV, or dm varies.

Since a spontaneous process takes place only when $\phi(P_1, V_1, P_2, V_2)$ increases, the reversible process defined as such does not take place in nature. However, we may define such a process as the mathematical limit of a sequence of spontaneous processes in which the rate of increase of $\phi(P_1, V_1, P_2, V_2)$ gradually decreases to zero. For example we may conceive the transfer of an amount of heat dQ equal to 1 cal. between two systems with a temperature

28

difference of 100°C., between another two systems with a temperature difference 99°C., etc., and we have a sequence of spontaneous processes. As the temperature difference decreases from 100°C. to 99°C., and so on, the rate of increase of the ϕ in one particular spontaneous process (taking the ϕ defined previously, $-|T_1 - T_2|$, for example) becomes smaller and smaller. In the limit when the temperature difference reduces to zero, the change of ϕ becomes zero, and such a transfer of heat (at equal temperature) is considered as a reversible process. In the limit when temperatures become equal no heat conduction can take place. On the other hand, as the temperature difference decreases, the time required for the transfer of 1 cal. of heat becomes longer, and in the limit we may say it takes an infinitely long time to transfer 1 cal. of heat. *A reversible process takes an infinitely long time to carry out.*

From a theoretical viewpoint the function $\phi(P_1, V_1, P_2, V_2)$ may be regarded as a function of the coordinates of a point in a four-dimensional space, and it is always conceivable that a sequence of adjacent points may be found such that the function ϕ has the same value at these points. If an interaction is introduced that allows the points to be accessible to one another we have a reversible process as defined. Since there is no increase in ϕ in the sequence the process will not proceed spontaneously. As the system will not proceed from each point to its neighboring points in the sequence spontaneously, each point represents an equilibrium state. Therefore we conclude that *a reversible process consists of a sequence of equilibrium states accessible to one another by varying the independent variable of the interaction.*

Once a sequence of adjacent, mutually accessible equilibrium states are given for a composite system we can cause an *actual* process to occur by exerting a small external influence on one of the two systems. For example we may add a small amount of heat to one system to raise the temperature so as to tip off the thermal equilibrium or exert a small pressure on one system to tip off the mechanical equilibrium. This external influence changes the thermodynamic state of the system and so changes its value of ϕ.

The value of ϕ now becomes different from that of the adjacent accessible state and a spontaneous process will take place leading the system to the adjacent state. By constantly exerting an external influence, a sequence of changes of state will follow. When the external influence is small, this sequence of changes of state follows very closely the sequence of equilibrium states. In the limit when the external influence is made approaching zero, this sequence of changes of state approaches the sequence of equilibrium states as a limit. This fact may be stated by saying that *a reversible process can actually take place in an approximate sense by applying an infinitesimal external influence.*

The external influence may also be applied so as to tip off the balance in the opposite direction. As a result the changes of states proceed in the reversed direction. In the limit the changes proceed along the sequence of equilibrium states in the reversed direction. Therefore we may say that *a reversible process may proceed in the reversed direction.* This is the reason for calling the process "*reversible.*" In the limit, because the *external* influence is reduced to zero, the process may be considered spontaneous. When the external influence is finite the process is not spontaneous, unless we include the external influence as the third thermodynamic system interacting with the two in a composite system of three components. Thus we consider the reversible process as an *idealized spontaneous process.*

When proceeding in the reversed direction the process passes through the same series of thermodynamic states as in the direct process, but in the reversed order; therefore *the sequence of changes of the thermodynamic variables in the reversed process retraces the sequence of changes in the direct process exactly but in the reversed order.* Furthermore, the amount of heat transferred and the amount of work performed at any stage in the reverse process are exactly the same as in the direct process, but they differ in sign. These results are summarized in the statement that the *reversible process may be reversed in every thermal and mechanical aspect.* These properties are not possessed by actual spontaneous

30

processes,* and for this reason the actual spontaneous processes are called *irreversible processes.*

We now consider the procedures by which a reversible process may be constructed. Take two thermodynamic systems which are allowed to interact with respect to the variable dQ or dV or dm. The interaction leads the composite system to an equilibrium state. We search in the neighborhood of the equilibrium state for an adjacent equilibrium state accessible by the interaction. When we find one we search for further equilibrium states in its neighborhood. The sequence of states so obtained constitutes a reversible process because the values of ϕ of all these states should be the same, otherwise the system will spontaneously change itself from one state to the other and cease to be in a state of equilibrium. Furthermore, by the application of an infinitesimal external influence one state may be changed to the other in one direction or in the reversed direction. Conversely, if there exists a sequence of adjacent states along which a spontaneous process may take place in either direction by infinitesimal external influences, the sequence constitutes a reversible process. This is another way of constructing a reversible process.

For two gases interacting thermally, mechanically, *and* diffusively the equilibrium state finally reached is such that the value of ϕ is an absolute maximum. In its neighborhood there exist no other equilibrium states. Therefore we cannot construct any reversible processes. As a rule there are no reversible processes for two arbitrary systems. Only when the systems have some peculiar properties does it become possible to construct a reversible process. Examples of reversible processes will be introduced later.

The analogy of ϕ with the gravitational potential may be carried out one step further. An equilibrium state with the maximum value of ϕ may be compared to an equilibrium position in the gravitational field where the gravitational potential has reached a minimum value. The reversible process may be compared

---

* For example, in the free expansion of a gas against vacuum, the pressure, work performed, and heat absorbed in the reversed process (compression) are not exactly the same as in the direct process (expansion).

to the case of neutral equilibrium in which there exists a sequence of equilibrium positions having the same value of gravitational potential. A slight external influence may cause one equilibrium position to change into another in either direction. Again neutral equilibrium does not occur often; it occurs only in special cases. Another point may be mentioned here. In gravitational equilibrium there is the exceptional case of unstable equilibrium in which gravitational potential is a maximum. Whether or not unstable equilibrium exists in thermodynamical phenomena has to be decided by experiment. However, if our basic assumption is correct physically, we may expect unstable equilibrium to appear.

The significance of the reversible process lies in the following fact: Since the sum $\phi_1 + \phi_2$ of the composite system is a constant in a reversible process, the change of ϕ_1 in the process must equal the negative of the change of ϕ_2. Thus

$$d\phi_1 = -d\phi_2. \tag{5}$$

If we know the change of ϕ of one thermodynamic system we can determine the change of ϕ of the other in the composite system. If we know the change of ϕ of a few special systems we may use these as standards to determine the change of ϕ of *any* other thermodynamic system by letting it interact with these standards in reversible processes. The purpose of introducing the reversible processes is to calculate the change of ϕ of a general thermodynamic system, there being no other physical purpose. The fact that the reversible process does not occur in nature is of no concern to us, since we do not intend to use the reversible process in any physical circumstances. That the reversible process is a mathematical concept based on a limiting process is also perfectly legitimate as long as it serves a mathematical purpose, i.e., the calculation of ϕ.

B. CHANGE OF ϕ OF A SYSTEM IN AN ADIABATIC REVERSIBLE PROCESS
We now consider a special type of reversible process in which only mechanical interaction takes place. This process is called the

32

adiabatic reversible process because no heat transfer takes place, dQ being constrained.

If one of the two interacting systems is a gas then we have the following situation. When the gas performs work it has to undergo an expansion. Usually an adiabatic expansion lowers the pressure of the gas. In order that the two systems remain in equilibrium after an expansion as required in the reversible process, the other thermodynamic system must undergo a lowering of pressure to exactly the same amount. On the other hand, the second system has an amount of work done on it adiabatically during the expansion of the gas. Thus, we require the other system to have the property that its pressure is to be lowered to a specific amount when an amount of work is done on it adiabatically. Ordinary thermodynamic systems do not have such a property—nearly all increase their pressure when an amount of work is done on them adiabatically. On the other hand, it is possible to construct deliberately a special thermodynamic system having exactly this property. Thus, we may take the other system interacting with a gas to be a weight placed on top of the piston covering the gas, the weight being under the action of a conservative force field (which may be of gravitational, electric, or mechanical origin) such that the force it exerts on the gas always equals the pressure of the gas as the latter expands. For a gas obeying a particular law of expansion, a force field matching the expansion can always be constructed. Therefore, we may always assume the availability of such a weight for the purpose of constructing a reversible process. In order that dQ be constrained, the weight must also be perfectly insulated against heat transfer. A thermodynamic system having all these properties is called a *perfectly insulated weight* or just a "weight." It is a *purely mechanical system*.

When a gas interacts with a perfectly insulated weight reversibly, the change of ϕ of the gas equals the negative of the change of ϕ of the weight. The weight is a special system; its change of ϕ can be determined. In the process the only change that affects the weight is a change of its position (change of its potential energy) which is

33

a purely mechanical variable; its thermodynamic variables are not changed. Since ϕ is a function of the thermodynamic variables only, the value of ϕ of the weight remains the same in the reversible process.* This means that, as far as spontaneous processes leading to equilibrium are concerned, a weight at a low position behaves exactly the same as the weight at a high position, provided that the thermodynamic variables are the same, which is self-evident. Since the value of ϕ of the weight is not changed, the value of ϕ of the gas remains the same in the adiabatic reversible process. The perfectly insulated weight thus serves as a standard† by which we can determine the change of ϕ of a gas in an adiabatic reversible process, and the result is that the value of ϕ remains the same. All equilibrium states of a gas which may be connected by an adiabatic reversible process have the same value of ϕ.

Take the perfect gas as an example. Its pressure, volume, and temperature in any state are related by the equation of state‡ of the perfect gas,

$$PV = nRT \tag{6}$$

where n is the molar number of the gas and R is the universal gas constant. Those states of the perfect gas connected by an adiabatic reversible process have the additional property that one may be changed to the other by the purely mechanical interaction with the weight (expansion or compression) without any transfer of heat. Therefore, the thermodynamic variables of these states obey the additional condition:

$$dQ = dU + pdV = 0. \tag{7}$$

* There is a simple physical interpretation of this result in the microscopic theory in a later chapter (p. 82).
† Besides the perfectly insulated weight we may also use the heat-independent surface tension of a specially conceived liquid as the purely mechanical variable of a system to absorb work in an adiabatic reversible process. It serves the same purpose.
‡ Equations of state are taken for granted as empirical information and not explained any further in thermodynamics; the derivation of the equation of state can be done only in microscopic theory.

34

From these two equations, (6) and (7), we deduce the following relation by straightforward calculation:

$$PV^\gamma = \text{const.} \tag{8}$$

where γ is the ratio of the specific heat at constant pressure to that at constant volume. The sequence of equilibrium states of the gas in an adiabatic reversible process obey Eq. (8), which may be represented by a curve in the P-V diagram. According to the previous result, the curve also connects the thermodynamic states having the same value of ϕ. For these reasons the curve is called an *adiabatic* curve or *iso-ϕ* curve. When the constant of Eq. (8) varies, we get a family of adiabatic or *iso-ϕ* curves.

For any other thermodynamic system, its equation of state and the adiabatic condition, Eq. (7), lead to the determination of a family of adiabatic curves. These represent the *iso-ϕ* curves of the system.

In the following we determine the change of ϕ from one *iso-ϕ* curve to another, then the value of ϕ of the thermodynamic system is completely defined, except for an additive constant, for all possible thermodynamic states (P, V).

C. CHANGE OF ϕ OF A SYSTEM IN AN ISOTHERMAL REVERSIBLE PROCESS

We now consider another special type of reversible process, in which an arbitrary thermodynamic system is allowed to take in heat (positive or negative) but its temperature is maintained at a constant value. When heat is added to a system, say, a gas, but temperature is not allowed to rise, the system usually expands and performs mechanical work. For the process to be reversible it is necessary that the work be done reversibly on a perfectly insulated weight. We need, in addition, a thermodynamic system serving the purpose of a heat reservoir to supply heat to the system by a thermal interaction. In order that the thermal interaction be reversible, the temperature of the reservoir must be the same as the system at all times, that is, the reservoir must be maintained at the same constant temperature. Since the reservoir is required to supply heat without lowering its temperature, it must have an infinitely large heat capacity, which requires an infinitely large amount of mass inside the reservoir. Again this may be conceived in the limit and the concept is a valid one as long as it is used for the purpose of making calculations. Since the sole purpose of the reservoir is to supply heat, we assume that it performs no mechanical work (if it is made of a gas, the volume is assumed to be kept at a constant value). Such a special thermodynamic system is called an *infinite heat reservoir*. It is a *purely thermal system*. Given a perfectly insulated weight and an infinite heat reservoir, any thermodynamic system, such as a gas, may interact with the former purely mechanically and simultaneous with the latter purely thermally at a fixed temperature in a reversible process. Such a process is called an *isothermal reversible process*.

An isothermal reversible process involves three thermodynamic systems—a weight, a reservoir, and a gas, for example. Thus, the potential of spontaneous transition of the composite system equals the sum $\phi_g + \phi_w + \phi_r$ of the potentials of spontaneous transition of the three components. Since the process is reversible, the sum $\phi_g + \phi_w + \phi_r$ remains constant. Because the value ϕ_w of the weight does not change in the process, we conclude that the change of ϕ of the gas equals the negative of the change of ϕ of the reservoir. Thus

$$d\phi_g = -d\phi_r. \qquad (9)$$

The reservoir is a special system, the change of ϕ of which may be determined explicitly in the following. Like the weight, the reservoir serves as a standard to calibrate the change of ϕ of other systems.

For the purpose of determining the change of ϕ of the reservoir $d\phi_r$ in an isothermal reversible process, we construct two identical thermodynamic systems, g and g', such as two gases of the same kind, same mass, same pressure P_1, and same volume V_1. Let the reservoir r interact with g in an isothermal reversible process; the necessary "weight" is always assumed to be there. An amount of heat dQ passes from the reservoir to the gas; as a result, the gas changes its pressure to P_2 and volume to V_2 (temperature remaining the same). The change of ϕ of the reservoir $d\phi_r$ equals the negative of that of the gas $d\phi_g$

$$d\phi_r = -d\phi_g. \tag{10}$$

Now, disconnect the reservoir from gas g and connect it to gas g' at (P_1, V_1). Since the reservoir has not changed its temperature in the first interaction, it is in thermal equilibrium with g' at (P_1, V_1), and we may allow an isothermal reversible process to take place by which g' changes from (P_1, V_1) to (P_2, V_2), the necessary "weight" being assumed. The change of ϕ of the reservoir in the second process $d\phi_{r'}$ equals the negative of that of the gas g', $d\phi_{g'}$

$$d\phi_{r'} = -d\phi_{g'}. \tag{11}$$

Since the changes of the thermodynamic states of g and g' are exactly the same, the corresponding changes of ϕ must be the same. Thus

$$d\phi_g = d\phi_{g'}. \tag{12}$$

Therefore, we have

$$d\phi_r = d\phi_{r'}. \tag{13}$$

In other words, the change of ϕ_r in the two successive processes is the same. Furthermore, the amount of heat absorbed by g' is the same as that of g; this leads to the result that the amount of heat leaving the reservoir is the same in the two processes. Therefore, the two successive processes taking place in the reservoir give rise to equal amount of change of ϕ corresponding to equal amount of heat transferred. Generalizing to 3, 4, . . . , n successive processes of the same kind, we conclude that the total change of ϕ of the reservoir in the n processes is proportional to the total amount of heat transferred, i.e.,

$$d\phi_r \propto dQ_r. \tag{14}$$

Since a reservoir, being a purely thermal system, can change its ϕ only by the transfer of heat, $d\phi_r$ is a function of dQ_r exclusively. The above result requires that the function be linear, i.e.,

$$d\phi_r = K_r dQ_r, \tag{15}$$

37

where K_r is a proportionality constant depending on the properties of the reservoir. To determine this constant, we consider a number of reservoirs r, r', r'', ..., differing in all properties except in temperature. Also, construct an equal number of identical thermodynamic systems g, g', g'', ..., and let each interact with one reservoir in an isothermal reversible process with the result that the state of the system changes from a common initial state (P_1, V_1) to a common final state (P_2, V_2). This is possible because all reservoirs have the same temperature and remain at the same temperature. The change of ϕ of each reservoir equals the negative of that of the corresponding system,

$$
\begin{aligned}
d\phi_r &= -d\phi_g, \\
d\phi_{r'} &= -d\phi_{g'}, \\
d\phi_{r''} &= -d\phi_{g''}, \\
&\cdots \cdots
\end{aligned}
\tag{16}
$$

Again the change of ϕ of all the systems g, g', g'', ..., is the same

$$
d\phi_g = d\phi_{g'} = d\phi_{g''} = \cdots,
\tag{17}
$$

therefore we conclude

$$
d\phi_r = d\phi_{r'} = d\phi_{r''} = \cdots.
\tag{18}
$$

In other words,

$$
K_r \, dQ_r = K_{r'} \, dQ_{r'} = K_{r''} \, dQ_{r''} = \cdots.
\tag{19}
$$

Since

$$
dQ_r = dQ_{r'} = dQ_{r''} = \cdots,
\tag{20}
$$

we conclude

$$
K_r = K_{r'} = K_{r''} = \cdots.
\tag{21}
$$

The reservoirs r, r', r'', ..., are assumed to be different in all properties except in temperature. The last equation thus means that K_r as a function of the properties of r is independent of all properties except temperature. In other words K_r is a function of temperature alone. The above result also implies that this function is a universal function, independent of the chemical properties of the reservoirs $r, r', r'', \ldots$. Thus we drop the indices $r, r', r'', \ldots$, and simply write $K(T)$.

Since the heat taken by the system dQ_g equals the negative of dQ_r, we deduce the following equation for the change of ϕ of any thermodynamic system in an isothermal reversible process:

$$d\phi_g = -d\phi_r = -K(T_r)\, dQ_r = K(T_g)\, dQ_g. \tag{22}$$

Here we have not specified any particular temperature scale. The above argument is valid for any empirical temperature scale since the only place temperature comes into consideration is in the specification of equal and constant temperature for all the reservoirs. In fact, the metric of the temperature scale does not enter the discussion. The above argument establishes the fact that K is a universal function of the temperature but that the explicit form of the function depends on the particular temperature scale used. Thus, we can always suitably choose the metric of the temperature scale to make the function $K(T)$ to appear in any mathematical form we wish. In particular, we introduce a temperature scale θ such that

$$K(\theta) = 1/\theta. \tag{23}$$

This scale is called the *thermodynamic temperature scale* or the *absolute temperature scale* or the *Kelvin scale*. As mentioned before, the term absolute is misleading; it actually means universal.

The next problem is to calibrate the thermodynamic temperature scale in terms of an empirical temperature scale which we actually use in the laboratory. For this purpose we take the perfect gas temperature scale as the empirical scale. This scale is defined by the perfect gas equation of state,

$$PV = nRT. \tag{24}$$

From the pressure and volume of a given amount of perfect gas the above equation enables us to calculate the temperature T in the perfect gas temperature scale. Incidentally, the condition that a real gas behave like a perfect gas may be realized by reducing the pressure of the gas, and therefore we have no experimental

39

difficulty of establishing the perfect gas temperature scale. To correlate θ with T, we need additional information concerning the thermodynamic properties of a perfect gas, besides its equation of state.* This is supplied by the result of the Joule-Thomson experiment, which may be stated thus: the internal energy U of a perfect gas is a function of the temperature alone. Together with the first law of thermodynamics, this result has the consequence that in an isothermal process the amount of heat taken into a perfect gas equals the amount of work performed by the gas. Therefore, the amount of heat dQ absorbed by a perfect gas in an isothermal reversible process may be calculated by the amount of work performed.

We first establish the *isothermal curves* in the *P-V* diagram which represent the sequence of thermodynamic states of a system undergoing an isothermal reversible process. These curves may be obtained by setting the temperature in the equation of state at a constant value. Each curve represents a sequence of adjacent equilibrium states all at the same temperature. By allowing the variables of the interaction to change, i.e., allowing heat transfer to take place between the system and the reservoir and allowing the gas to perform work on the weight, the system may change from one state to the other reversibly. Thus, the curve represents an isothermal reversible process. The work done by the gas in such a process is given by the area under the isothermal curve. This work equals the gain of energy of the weight because the force the weight experiences in the reversible process equals the equilibrium pressure of the gas, which is represented by the isothermal curve. This is not the case if the process is not reversible. For example, when a gas expands into a vacuum the work done "on the vacuum" is zero; the area under the equilibrium curve does not equal the work performed on the other system (it does so only when the process is reversible).

* This does not mean that we need additional postulate in our theoretical structure. We need only the empirical information of the perfect gas so that we may establish the relation between the thermodynamic temperature scale and an empirical temperature scale based on the perfect gas.

40

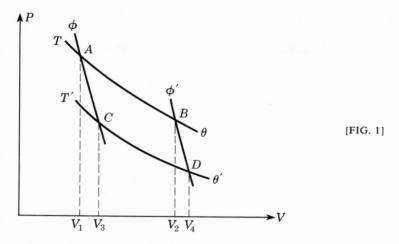

[FIG. 1]

From the isothermal curves of the perfect gas represented by the equation

$$PV = \text{const.} \tag{25}$$

we can calculate the work performed by the gas by taking the area under the curve

$$W = \int_{V_1}^{V_2} P \, dV = \int_{V_1}^{V_2} \frac{nRT}{V} \, dV = nRT \ln \frac{V_2}{V_1}. \tag{26}$$

As discussed previously, this work equals the amount of heat dQ_g absorbed by the perfect gas in the isothermal reversible process. Therefore, we have the change of ϕ of the gas during the process as follows:

$$d\phi = \frac{dQ_g}{\theta} = \frac{nRT}{\theta} \ln \frac{V_2}{V_1}. \tag{27}$$

We now consider two adiabatic curves ϕ, ϕ' and two isothermal curves θ, θ'. The value of ϕ remains constant along an adiabatic curve and θ remains constant along an isothermal curve. Points A and C in Fig. 1, being on the same adiabatic curve, have the same value of ϕ. Thus

$$\phi_A = \phi_C. \tag{28}$$

41

Similarly,

$$\phi_B = \phi_D. \tag{29}$$

From these two equations we deduce

$$\phi_B - \phi_A = \phi_D - \phi_C. \tag{30}$$

On the other hand, from Eq. (27) we get

$$\phi_B - \phi_A = \frac{nRT}{\theta} \ln \frac{V_2}{V_1}, \tag{31}$$

$$\phi_D - \phi_C = \frac{nRT'}{\theta'} \ln \frac{V_4}{V_3}. \tag{32}$$

Equations (30), (31), and (32) lead to the following equation:

$$\frac{nRT}{\theta} \ln \frac{V_2}{V_1} = \frac{nRT'}{\theta'} \ln \frac{V_4}{V_3} \tag{33}$$

For a perfect gas, the temperature versus volume relation in an adiabatic process, which may be deduced from Eq. (6) and Eq. (8), is

$$TV^{\gamma-1} = \text{const.} \tag{34}$$

Therefore we have the following relations:

$$TV_1^{\gamma-1} = T'V_3^{\gamma-1}, \tag{35}$$

$$TV_2^{\gamma-1} = T'V_4^{\gamma-1}. \tag{36}$$

As a result,

$$\frac{V_2}{V_1} = \frac{V_4}{V_3}. \tag{37}$$

By making use of Eq. (37), Eq. (33) leads to

$$\frac{T}{\theta} = \frac{T'}{\theta'}. \tag{38}$$

In other words, the thermodynamic temperature scale differs from the perfect gas temperature scale only by a proportionality constant. This constant is made equal to unity by choosing the unit degree of the thermodynamic temperature scale to be the same as the perfect gas scale. Thus we have completely identified the thermodynamic scale with the perfect gas scale. From now on we shall make no distinction between the two scales.

The change of ϕ of a thermodynamic system in an isothermal reversible process is

$$d\phi_g = \frac{dQ_g}{T}. \tag{39}$$

By the isothermal process we can calculate the difference of ϕ between any two adiabatic curves; thus we are able to map out the value of ϕ for every point on the P-V diagram. The value of ϕ is determined except for an additive constant which will be left undetermined in the macroscopic theory (second law of thermodynamics). The task of determining the values of ϕ for all thermodynamic states of a system is now accomplished. The value depends only on the position of the representative point in the P-V diagram, as ϕ is solely a function of the thermodynamic variables.

We may note that the function ϕ so constructed has a mathematical form identical with the entropy function in the conventional formulation and is therefore identified with entropy.

D. CHANGE OF ϕ OF A SYSTEM IN A GENERAL REVERSIBLE PROCESS
We now consider the possibility of a general reversible process in which the state of a system changes along an arbitrary curve AB in the P-V diagram (Fig. 2). Such a curve connects a sequence of equilibrium states. Let us see under what conditions a process along such a curve may take place reversibly. First of all, the work performed by the system must be absorbed by a weight reversibly. Also, we need a reservoir with its temperature varying in such a way that the reservoir is always in thermal equilibrium with the system. Such a condition may be fulfilled by using a gas as the reservoir and letting another "weight" interact with the reservoir mechanically in such a manner that the temperature of the reservoir changes as desired. Theoretically, it is always possible

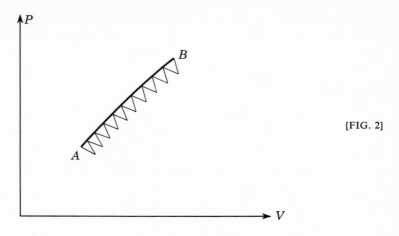

[FIG. 2]

to conceive such a weight-constrained reservoir. Thus, a general reversible process along any path is theoretically possible.

The change of ϕ of a system along such a path may be calculated as follows: For an infinitesimal change along this path, in which the amount of heat taken into the system is dQ and the temperature does not change much from the average value T, the change of ϕ equals dQ/T plus an infinitesimal of a higher order. The total change of ϕ from A to B is thus a summation of dQ/T plus an infinitesimal. When dQ approaches zero the summation approaches the limit expressed by the following integral:

$$\phi_B - \phi_A = \int_A^B \frac{dQ}{T} \tag{40}$$

In evaluating the integral, we have to have a knowledge of dQ along the path AB which is different for different thermodynamic systems. This is to be taken from the empirical information specifying the system, e.g. the equation of state and the specific heat at constant volume C_V.

An alternate approach is to replace the curve AB in Fig. 2 by a zigzag curve consisting of a series of isothermal and adiabatic curves and then to let the zigzag curve approach the smooth curve

44

as the limit.* Thus a knowledge of the isothermal and adiabatic processes is sufficient for any calculation of entropy, as previously mentioned.

Between any two points A, B in the P-V diagram we can draw many curves, and the difference $\phi_B - \phi_A$ may be calculated along any curve in a reversible process. Furthermore, the calculations along different curves should give the same result, since ϕ is a function of the thermodynamic variables and therefore $\phi_B - \phi_A$ depends only on the position of the two points A and B. The analogy with the calculation of the gravitational potential (or electric potential) is obvious. Therefore the amount of heat dQ absorbed reversibly between two adjacent points cannot vary arbitrarily over the P-V plane. The variation must be subject to the condition that $\int dQ/T$ is independent of the path of integration. As a result, the thermal properties of a thermodynamic system, such as the specific heat, the latent heat, etc., cannot vary arbitrarily with respect to the thermodynamic variables. Here we have arrived at a physical consequence of our basic assumption. If our basic assumption is correct, we are able to deduce some information on the thermal properties of matter from which many applications of thermodynamics arise. Mathematically, the fact that $\int dQ/T$ is independent of the path of integration is equivalent to saying that dQ/T is an exact differential† with respect to the independent variables, say, P and V. For an expression

* The length of the zigzag curve does not approach the length of the smooth curve as its limit and therefore the substitution requires justification. The dQ along the smooth curve and that along the "saw-tooth" differ by an infinitesimal of higher order because the corresponding dU is the same and the corresponding PdV differs by an infinitesimal of higher order. Of course, T also differs by an infinitesimal. Therefore $d\phi$ differs by an infinitesimal of higher order.

† On the other hand dQ itself is not an exact differential because $\int_A^B dQ$ is not only dependent on the position of A and B but also dependent on the path of integration, as may be seen easily in the case of the perfect gas (compare path AB with $ACDB$ in Fig. 1). The inexact differential dQ is usually expressed by δQ or dQ. We use the notation d for all infinitesimal quantities (exact or inexact). $d\phi$ is exact because ϕ is a function of the thermodynamic variables to start with. The factor $1/T$, which makes the product dQ/T an exact differential, is called an integration factor of dQ.

45

$F(x, y) \, dx + G(x, y) \, dy$ to be an exact differential $F(x, y)$ and $G(x, y)$ must satisfy

$$\frac{\partial F(x, y)}{\partial y} = \frac{\partial G(x, y)}{\partial x}.$$ (41)

Applying this equation to the differential dQ/T we obtain the mathematical expression of the condition imposed on the thermal properties of matter by the basic assumption. Applications may be worked out mathematically. We will return to this point later.

E. CHANGE OF ϕ OF A SYSTEM IN A DIFFUSIVE REVERSIBLE PROCESS
The previous discussion enables us to determine the value of ϕ of a system as a function of the thermodynamic variables such as P and V, except for an undetermined constant. The method, however, does not specify how the value of ϕ changes in a diffusive inter-action. For the purpose of determining this change we introduce a diffusive reversible process.

Consider two different gases A and B of equal temperature placed in two cylinders of equal volume V. The pressures may not be equal because the masses may not be. Each cylinder has one end covered by a semipermeable membrane which is permeable only to the gas inside the other cylinder. The two cylinders are fitted together as shown in Fig. 3 to allow a telescopic motion. Notice that the side of cylinder A goes through the membrane of cylinder B; a special mechanism must be provided to keep the membrane of B rigidly fixed to the cylinder B disregarding the telescopic motion of cylinder A. This can be done by mechanical devices or magnetic devices, and such a mechanism is always assumed. At the beginning of the process the two membranes coincide and the

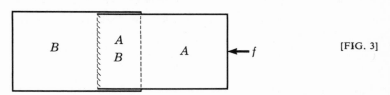

[FIG. 3]

46

two gases are separate. Now both gases start to diffuse through the membranes into the space between the two membranes until the partial pressures of A and B in the space between the membranes equal the pressures of the unmixed gases in the cylinders A and B respectively. Equilibrium is then established. We now recognize the fact that the two cylinders can be in equilibrium at any position throughout the telescopic motion. For the position shown in Fig. 3, diffusive equilibrium of gas A and gas B will be established spontaneously, Once this is established, mechanical equilibrium follows. The net pressure on the membrane of cylinder A is the partial pressure of the gas A between the two membranes since the pressures due to B on both sides of this membrane are equal and opposite to each other. Since the partial pressure of A equals the pressure in cylinder A, the force acting on membrane A equals that on the other end of cylinder A. Therefore, cylinder A is in mechanical equilibrium. The same holds for cylinder B. The above argument is valid for any other relative positions of the two cylinders. Thus, we have a sequence of equilibrium states associated with the telescopic motion. When we apply an infinitesimal force f on cylinder A, the latter begins to be telescoped into cylinder B and the process passes through the sequence of equilibrium states until finally the membranes reach the bottom and the two gases are completely mixed in the space between the membranes. When we reverse the direction of this infinitesimal force, cylinder A begins to be telescoped out of cylinder B until finally the two membranes coincide and the mixture of A and B is completely separated into two pure gases. Letting force f approach zero, we deduce that the equilibrium states in the sequence have equal values of ϕ, and thus form a reversible process. As a result, the value of ϕ of the mixture of A and B equals the value of ϕ of the composite system of two separate gases, each having the same volume as the mixture and each having a pressure equal to the corresponding partial pressure in the mixture. This result enables us to calculate the value of ϕ of a mixture in terms of the component systems and thereby extends the range of application of the law of spontaneous processes to systems of mixtures and to the diffusion process. This also completes our program of determining the explicit form of ϕ for a general thermodynamic system.

Two remarks may be made here. One concerns the semipermeable membrane. As mentioned before, *some* semipermeable membranes do exist in nature, and therefore it is legitimate to assume the existence of such a membrane for *every* gas solely for the purpose of calculation (not for other physical purposes). From the viewpoint of microscopic theory, a semipermeable membrane is a porous material, the pores of which allow the molecules of some gases to pass, but not the molecules of others. In the above argument, we need two membranes, each permeable to one kind of molecules, but not to the other. A conceptual difficulty may arise at this point. If the pores of one membrane are large enough to pass the larger of the two kinds of molecules, how can they stop the passage of the smaller kind? The answer lies in the fact that not only the size, but also the shape of the pores contributes to the screening of molecules by the membrane. To exaggerate, we may conceive two kinds of molecules, one having the shape of a left-handed screw and the other a right-handed screw. The pores of the two membranes have the shapes of a left-handed screw groove and a right-handed screw groove, respectively. Obviously, only one type of molecule can pass through one particular membrane. As long as the two kinds of molecules are different physically, we can always conceive the pores to be such that the two kinds of molecules react with them differently and thus one membrane is permeable only to one type of molecule. Thus, a mixture of two isotopes may still be separable conceptually in spite of their having the same size, same shape, and same chemical properties, because their nuclear properties, such as the nuclear magnetic moment, are different.

This discussion leads to the well-known Gibbs paradox. The above argument for separating a mixture remains valid no matter how minute the difference between the two gases may be. It seems as though it remains valid in the limit when the difference of the two kinds of molecules is reduced to zero—i.e., they become identical. When A and B are identical and have the same partial pressure, the initial state (the mixture) and the final state (the separate gases) of the process discussed above *do not* have the same value of ϕ because the final state has a volume twice as large and a pressure twice as small—an equilibrium state connected to the initial state (now a pure gas) by an isothermal reversible process along which ϕ is not constant. Thus the paradox. From our point of view, we may say that as soon as the two gases become identical, no semipermeable membranes may be conceived conceptually and the argument given previously cannot stand. Actually the previous argument has a practical significance in applications only when a separation or a distinction of the two gases is actually involved in the problem. In most chemical reactions two isotopes behave exactly the same and no distinction or separation is ever made. Hence, in these reactions all gases are treated as pure in spite of the fact that they are all isotopic mixtures. Furthermore, the continuous variation of the properties of molecules as assumed in the paradox is not a legitimate concept because it is contrary to the experimental fact that atoms and isotopes are discrete, not continuous from one to another. The atomic number and the mass number can take on only integral values, not fractions; there is no other atom between two neighboring atoms in the periodic table, e.g., hydrogen and helium. Furthermore, atomic and molecular properties are usually quantized, not continuously variable.

The second remark concerns the conventional treatment of the entropy of a mixture. There the entropy change is defined as the heat intake dQ in a reversible process divided by the thermodynamic temperature T. Based on this definition the Clausius theorem or the Kelvin inequality is then derived. The entropy is defined for a change of thermodynamic state of a pure system; the meaning of dQ/T in the diffusive reversible process is not yet defined. To say that the change of entropy is zero in the diffusive reversible process because dQ is zero in this process actually

49

involves the unannounced generalization of the concept entropy to a new process and the smuggling into the theory of new physical postulates. The real reason that the change of entropy is zero in this process (which we have discussed) was not discussed in the conventional treatment. The difficulty originates from the fact that the conventional formulation starts from a special case (heat engine) and then works into a general theory (spontaneous processes). Generalizations must be made in such an approach but the additional physical concepts and postulates were not clearly stated when introduced, which caused confusion and logical difficulties. Here we start from the general case and thus avoid the difficulties involved in the classical formulation.

F. VERIFICATION

Assuming the additivity of ϕ we have determined the explicit form of the function ϕ for all thermodynamic states accessible by thermal, mechanical, and diffusive interactions. We now must verify that the function ϕ so determined actually has the property we required of ϕ, i.e., the total value of ϕ of a composite system always increases in spontaneous processes. According to our previous discussion, we have to show that ϕ of the composite system increases in thermal interactions, in mechanical interactions, and in diffusive interactions. Verification is necessary because we have not proved the additivity at the beginning. Once verified, the additivity is proved automatically.

First we introduce a special spontaneous process involving only mechanical interaction, called the *dissipative process*, in which the kinetic energy of a purely mechanical system is converted into the internal energy of another system interacting with it. A concrete example is a perfectly insulated wheel having a certain amount of rotational energy placed in a viscous fluid of a fixed volume. The stirring wheel of a calorimeter is a rough approximation. The viscous force provides the mechanical interaction between the wheel and the fluid. It is a spontaneous process—the rotation of the wheel becomes slower and slower and eventually comes to a stop, i.e., mechanical equilibrium with the fluid is established. As the process proceeds, the wheel loses kinetic energy; the fluid gains internal energy. The process cannot be reversed in every mechanical and thermal aspect because by reversing the direction of turning of the wheel the internal energy of the fluid cannot be changed back to the kinetic energy of the wheel. The value of ϕ of the wheel does not change because the thermodynamic variables of the wheel are not changed (perfectly heat-insulated); the change of its kinetic energy is a change of a purely mechanical variable. On the other hand, the value of ϕ of the fluid increases, because the final state with a higher internal energy at the same volume may be reached by a reversible process in which heat is continuously added to the system, and $\int dQ/T$ is positive. Therefore, we conclude that *in the dissipative process the ϕ of the composite system increases.*

We now prove that in spontaneous processes due to thermal interaction the value of ϕ of the composite system always increases. We shall show that the final state reached in such a spontaneous process can be reached from the initial state by a reversible process followed by a dissipative process; along this path we are able to calculate the change of ϕ. As the change of ϕ is zero in the reversible process and is positive in the dissipative process, the increase of ϕ in this spontaneous process may then be proved.

Consider the process of transfer of heat by conduction, in which an amount of heat Q_1 leaves an infinite heat reservoir at a high temperature T_1 and enters another at a low temperature T_2. The final state arrived at in this process may be reached in two steps as above. The first is a reversible process consisting of four steps:* (1) The reservoir T_1 interacts isothermally with a newly introduced thermodynamic system by which Q_1 passes reversibly from the reservoir to the system. (2) The system then undergoes an adiabatic expansion to lower its temperature to T_2. (3) The system interacts isothermally with the reservoir T_2 until the system has reached a value of ϕ equal to its initial value before the starting

* This reversible process is the well-known Carnot cycle.

51

of the first step. Since in the first step the system increases its value of ϕ by Q_1/T_1 and in the second step the value of ϕ does not change, the necessary change in the third step is to let an amount of heat Q_2 pass from the system to the reservoir T_2 such that

$$\frac{Q_2}{T_2} = \frac{Q_1}{T_1}. \tag{42}$$

(4) Finally, the system undergoes an adiabatic process to return to its initial state. This is possible because no change of ϕ is involved. In the four reversible processes the necessary "weights" are always assumed. At the completion of the four steps, these weights will accumulate a total amount of mechanical energy W equal to $Q_1 - Q_2$ according to the first law of thermodynamics. Since T_1 is greater than T_2 the above equation asserts that Q_1 is greater than Q_2; therefore W is positive. At the completion of the reversible process we let a dissipative process take place by which the amount of mechanical energy W possessed by the weights is dissipated in reservoir T_2. This may be accomplished by transferring the mechanical energy to a spinning wheel and dropping it in reservoir T_2. Reservoir T_2 gains heat Q_2 in the reversible process and gains internal energy W in the dissipative process; the total gain is thus $Q_2 + W$, which equals Q_1. The weights and the system all return to their initial states. Thus, the final state of the spontaneous process is arrived at by the reversible process followed by the dissipative process. The increase of ϕ is therefore proved.

In any thermal interaction, when an amount of heat dQ leaves a system at T_1 and enters another at T_2 the change of ϕ may be analyzed in the same way. Therefore in any thermal interaction the value of ϕ of the composite system increases.

The proof for the increase of ϕ in spontaneous processes due to mechanical interaction may be carried out in a similar manner. Take the example given at the beginning of this chapter. Two gases of different pressure separated by a frictionless piston interact until their pressures become equal. The final state of this spontaneous process may be reached by a reversible process followed by a dissipative process. In the reversible process the difference of pressure of the two gases is balanced off by the pressure of a purely mechanical system which absorbs part of the mechanical work produced in the expansion process. In the dissipative process this part of mechanical energy is changed into internal energy of the two gases in a way such that the final state of the spontaneous process is reached. The change of ϕ may be calculated along this path; the change is zero in the reversible process and positive in the dissipative process. Thus, the value of ϕ increases in spontaneous processes due to mechanical interaction.

For spontaneous processes due to diffusive interaction we consider the diffusion of two different gases of the same volume V and pressure P by removing the partition separating them or making the partition permeable to both gases. Equal pressure is required to avoid mechanical interaction. Equal volume is assumed for convenience of discussion. As a result of the diffusion process, the system changes into a uniform mixture of the two gases having the same pressure P and a volume equal to $2V$. This final state of the process may be reached by a reversible process followed by a dissipative process. The reversible process consists of two steps. The first is a process which has been discussed before: by making use of two semipermeable membranes the two separate gases change into a mixture with a volume equal to V and therefore a pressure equal to $2P$ (assuming both are perfect gases). The second is an isothermal reversible process by which the mixture expands to a volume of $2V$ and a pressure of P. In the second process, the change of ϕ of the reservoir is $-(Q/T)$, that of the mixture is Q/T. At the same time the "weight" gains mechanical energy equal to Q. The dissipative process that follows causes the mechanical energy of the weight to be changed into internal energy of the reservoir. In so doing, the reservoir and the weight return to their initial states exactly and the final state of the spontaneous process is reached. In the reversible process the total change of ϕ is zero; in the dissipative process the total change is positive (actually

53

equal to Q/T for the reservoir). Thus the total change of ϕ is positive.*

We have proved that the function ϕ determined in the previous sections for a composite system does have the property required of ϕ_t, ϕ_m, and ϕ_d. Therefore, an additive function ϕ does exist to serve as the potential of spontaneous transition and the explicit form of this function is determined to within an additive constant by Eq. (40).

The above discussion, incidentally, also throws light on the engineering problem of converting heat into mechanical work. In the reversible process no useful work is lost forever because it can always be recovered by reversing the process. In the dissipative process this is not so. Therefore in all spontaneous processes and thus in the changing of the universe as a whole the total amount of useful work tends to decrease; the universe is running down all the time.

The examples discussed here also appear in the classical formulation in establishing the law of increase of entropy. However the discussion on spontaneous processes in the classical formulation forms an independent addition to the Kelvin-Clausius second law. In our treatment, the latter need not be postulated; it can be derived (see Chapter 4, Section 1).

We are now in a position to identify the additive function ϕ with the entropy function in the conventional formulation. The entropy of a system is defined by $\int dQ/T$ where dQ is the amount of heat taken into the system along a reversible process. We find that in all reversible processes involving thermal, mechanical, and diffusive interactions, the entropy function calculated according to this definition agrees with the ϕ function determined in the previous sections except for an additive constant. Furthermore, the ϕ function does possess the properties ascribed to the entropy function, i.e., it is a function of the thermodynamic variables and it always increases in spontaneous processes. From now on this

* It may be proved that this conclusion holds also for the diffusion of two gases of different pressure and different volume.

54

additive form of the potential of spontaneous transition is called the entropy of the thermodynamic system and is denoted by the conventional symbol S.

As an example we determine the entropy of a perfect gas as a function of its thermodynamic variables T and P, say. The entropy of n moles of perfect gas may be calculated as follows:

$$S = \int \frac{dQ}{T}$$

$$= \int \frac{dU}{T} + \int \frac{P\,dv}{T}$$

$$= \int nC_v \frac{dT}{T} + \int \frac{nR\,dT - V\,dP}{T}$$

$$= nC_p \ln T - nR \ln P + \text{const.}$$

$$= n(C_p \ln T - R \ln P + k),$$

where C_v and C_p are the specific heats at constant volume and pressure, respectively, and k is a constant. That the constant of integration is proportional to the molar number may be seen as follows. Divide the gas into two halves which have the same value of T and P. In order that the sum of the entropy of the two halves equals the entropy of the whole (entropy is an additive quantity) the integration constant must be proportional to the molar number. The entropy may also be expressed in terms of other independent variables; the particular form given above will be used in applications later.

4. Mathematical deductions

The law of spontaneous processes (the second law of thermodynamics) asserts that in any spontaneous (irreversible) process leading to a stable equilibrium, the total entropy of the interacting systems must increase. This leads immediately to the equilibrium condition, which may be stated as follows: the necessary and

55

sufficient condition of thermodynamic equilibrium is that the total entropy of the interacting systems be a maximum with respect to the variations of dQ, dV, dm, . . . , consistent with the constraints of the systems,

$$dS = 0, \quad d^2S < 0. \tag{43}$$

When the entropy function is given explicitly in terms of the thermodynamic variables, the equilibrium condition enables us to determine the relations existing among the thermodynamic variables of the systems at equilibrium. In practical applications a thermodynamic system, which may be a composite system, may interact with the surroundings—the atmosphere and so on. In applying the above condition, the surroundings must be included in the composite system as a party of the interaction. Depending on the conditions existing between the system and the surroundings, we may introduce other thermodynamic functions (free energy, thermodynamical potential) to express equilibrium conditions for various processes. These are contained in a number of mathematical theorems, which make it more convenient to apply the equilibrium condition to practical problems. Since this book is concerned primarily with the physical principles of thermodynamics, we shall not discuss these mathematical deductions here.

The law of spontaneous processes also asserts that in the idealized spontaneous process, the reversible process leading to neutral equilibrium, the total entropy remains constant. It is the application to reversible processes that leads to the identification of $\phi_B - \phi_A$ to $\int_A^B dQ/T$ and thus to the conclusion that $\int_A^B dQ/T$ is independent of the path of integration between the limits A and B. As mentioned before, this condition imposes a limitation on the amount of heat dQ that can be taken into a thermodynamic system along a reversible path. Thus, it enables us to predict certain relations among the thermal properties of matter, such as the specific heats and the latent heats. Again, this prediction is facilitated by a set of mathematical theorems derived from the mathematical condition that dQ/T is an exact differential, which has a form like that of Eq. (41). The results of these theorems are called *thermodynamical relations*. Among them are the four *Maxwell relations*. Again, we do not discuss the mathematical details of these theorems because we are primarily concerned with the physical principles.

We have outlined how the physical contents of the law of spontaneous processes may be elaborated mathematically and may be expressed in forms more convenient to use in actual applications. The two areas of application, the irreversible processes and the reversible processes, are covered by two sets of mathematical theorems. Incidentally, the two parts are derived here from a single principle on a unified basis, while in the conventional formulation they are more or less separate. In both processes we make use of the equilibrium condition

$$dS = 0. \tag{44}$$

In the irreversible process this equation refers to stable equilibrium while in the reversible process it refers to neutral equilibrium. Thus, it is not surprising to find that a result deduced from a thermodynamical relation may also be deduced from an equilibrium condition. One example is the Clausius-Clapeyron equation, which may be deduced from a Maxwell relation as well as from the equilibrium condition of the isothermal-isobaric processes. The equilibrium in this case may be regarded as neutral or stable, depending on which variables are constrained.

IV

APPLICATIONS

As we are primarily concerned with the physical principles of thermodynamics, the following applications are given mainly for the purpose of illustrating the principles. This chapter is not intended to be a complete and balanced treatment of the various applications of the thermodynamical laws.

1. Engineering applications

Of particular interest is the application of thermodynamics to engineering. The efficiency of heat engines, which is the starting point of thermodynamics in the conventional formulation, will now appear as a deduction of the law of spontaneous processes. We define a heat engine as a machine which converts heat from a reservoir at a fixed temperature T_1 to mechanical work by a cyclic change of the thermodynamic state of a material system called the *working substance* (such as steam in a steam engine). After each cycle of change the working substance is brought back to the original state and the net change that takes place is the conversion of a part of the heat taken out of the reservoir into mechanical work. The cycle may be repeated indefinitely to convert heat into work continuously. In order that a finite amount of heat be taken out of the reservoir, the working substance must be made to absorb heat at a constant temperature which causes an expansion.

To bring the substance back to the original state, some compression is necessary. This cannot be done by adiabatic compressions alone because an adiabatic curve intercepts an isothermal curve only at one point. Thus, we need some kind of compression in which heat transfer is allowed. In such a compression the working substance rejects heat to a cooling system called the *condenser*. Thus, the condenser is an unavoidable part of the cyclic engine. To simplify the matter we consider the condenser to be maintained at a fixed temperature T_2. The simplest way for the working substance to change from the isothermal curve at temperature T_1 to that at T_2 (and for it to return to T_1) is by an adiabatic process. Thus in general, the working substance changes in cycles of four steps: an isothermal process at temperature T_1, an adiabatic process from T_1 to T_2, an isothermal process at T_2, and an adiabatic process from T_2 to T_1.

We next define a *reversible engine* as an engine in which all thermodynamical processes are reversible processes. When the processes consist of the above four steps, the reversible engine is called a *Carnot engine* and the cycle is called a *Carnot cycle*. In order that the four processes be reversible, a number of "weights" are necessary; these are parts of the machine that produce mechanical work. Since after one complete cycle the working substance returns to the original state, the net change of its entropy is zero. Letting Q_1 be the heat taken into the substance at temperature T_1 and Q_2 be the heat rejected by the substance at temperature T_2, we may write this condition as follows:

$$\frac{Q_1}{T_1} - \frac{Q_2}{T_2} = 0. \tag{45}$$

The work performed (on the "weights") in one cycle of operation, according to the first law, is

$$W = Q_1 - Q_2. \tag{46}$$

In order to make the work positive, Q_1 must be greater than Q_2 and thus T_1 must be greater than T_2. Therefore the condenser must be maintained at a low temperature. The efficiency η of the Carnot engine, defined as the ratio of W to Q_1, is thus

$$\eta = \frac{W}{Q_1} = \frac{Q_1 - Q_2}{Q_1} = \frac{T_1 - T_2}{T_1}. \tag{47}$$

The important thing in this result is that the efficiency of the Carnot engine is determined only by the temperatures of the reservoir and the condenser. It is independent of the working substance and the length of the isothermal process of the cycle. Thus all Carnot engines using different working substances operating between the same reservoir and the same condenser have the same efficiency. Furthermore, all reversible engines allowed to exchange heat only with a reservoir and a condenser of fixed temperatures must operate on a Carnot cycle, because from one isothermal process to the other no other thermal interaction is provided, i.e., the process must be adiabatic. Thus we arrive at the conclusion that all reversible engines operating between two fixed temperatures have the same efficiency. This is the first part of the *Carnot theorem*.

As reversible processes are idealized processes and proceed infinitely slowly, all actual engines are not reversible because they all proceed at a finite rate. Thus we have to take up the problem of the efficiency of the actual engines. Let us consider how an actual engine differs from a reversible engine and how these differences change the efficiency.

First, in order to transfer heat from the reservoir to the working substance at a finite rate, there must exist a finite temperature difference between the reservoir and the substance so that a spontaneous process of heat transfer may take place. Therefore, in order to produce the same amount of work from the same amount of heat, an actual engine requires a higher temperature for the reservoir and a lower temperature for the condenser. Such changes of the temperatures T_1 and T_2 would cause an increase of the efficiency of the Carnot engine operating between them, according to Eq. (47). Thus the efficiency of the actual engine is smaller than that of the reversible engine.

Second, for the piston to move with a finite speed, the pressure that the working substance exerts on the piston must be greater than the pressure of the load, on which mechanical work is done, so that a spontaneous process ensues. The work done on the load is always smaller than the work performed by the substance (the difference becomes the kinetic energy of the piston which is dissipated into internal energy by viscous forces). The two are the same in a reversible engine. Thus the work done on the load in actual engines is smaller than that in reversible engines. Therefore, the efficiency of an actual engine is smaller than that of the reversible engine.

Third, in actual engines heat from the reservoir may be lost by conduction, convection, and radiation to surroundings in the operation of the engine. (Again, a spontaneous process is involved.) The heat loss causes a further reduction of the efficiency.

Finally, in actual engines friction is unavoidable and a part of the mechanical work performed is lost by friction. (Again, a spontaneous process is involved.) This loss further reduces the efficiency.

We thus conclude that the efficiency of an actual engine is lower than that of the reversible engine operating between the same reservoir and the same condenser. This is the second part of the Carnot theorem. Notice that in each case the reduction in efficiency is invariably caused by a spontaneous process. Since in actual engines spontaneous processes always occur, the efficiency is always lower than that of Eq. (47). For the same reason, the cycle cannot be reversed in the sense that a reversible process is reversed. Thus actual engines are said to be *irreversible*.

It may be remarked that in the conventional formulation the concept of entropy is established after a discussion of the effects of these four factors on the heat engine. Obviously, the heat engine is dragged in unnecessarily—the entropy concept is based on the spontaneous processes, not on the engine.

61

The above discussion also leads to a conclusion: the condition that an engine (or a process) be reversible is that there be no temperature gradient, no pressure gradient, no heat loss (due to conduction, convection, and radiation), and no work loss (due to friction and viscosity).

When a reversible engine operates with its cycle reversed, all the quantities Q_1, Q_2, W change sign but do not change magnitude. The machine then performs as a refrigerator.

The practical significance of the efficiency of reversible engines lies in the fact that this is the limit of the efficiency of actual engines and refrigerators.

From the Carnot theorem, we can deduce the Clausius statement of the second law of thermodynamics (and thus the Kelvin statement) in a limited form: heat cannot be made to flow automatically from a low temperature reservoir to a high temperature reservoir by performing cyclic changes of the thermodynamic state of a thermodynamic system. The original statement, which does not include the limitation "by cyclic changes of the thermodynamic state" is more general. Without such a limitation, the question of Maxwell's demon and similar questions arise which are actually irrelevant to thermodynamics. As far as thermodynamics is concerned the limited form is all we need to deduce the significant results of thermodynamics from the second law. Whether the general statement is correct or not is an "engineering" problem, the solution of which lies in statistical mechanics.

2. Physical applications

The engineering applications discussed above are based on the fact that dQ/T along a reversible process is an exact differential. We now discuss a few physical applications based on the same fact.

The first concerns the change of boiling point of a liquid with respect to an increase of pressure. The boiling point is actually the temperature at which the saturated vapor pressure of the liquid

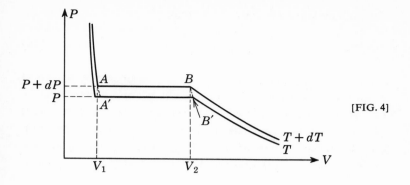

[FIG. 4]

equals the external pressure the liquid is exposed to (i.e., the pressure of the air above the liquid surface). Only when the saturated vapor pressure becomes as large as the external pressure does the formation of bubbles of saturated vapor inside the liquid become possible; then the liquid boils. Thus, the physical problem is reduced to the determination of the change of the saturated vapor pressure with respect to the temperature. To do this, we consider the saturated vapor as a thermodynamic system. This system is not just a gas or a liquid; it is a gas and a liquid interacting with each other, with their thermodynamic variables constrained in such a way that the vapor is always saturated. This is certainly a very special kind of thermodynamic system with a very peculiar equation of state. In Fig. 4, where we show the isothermal curves of an imperfect gas (liquification takes place only for imperfect gases), the saturated vapor pressure at a given temperature is given by the ordinate of the horizontal section of the corresponding isothermal curve. To determine its temperature dependence, let us consider two neighboring isothermal curves at temperatures T and $T + dT$, the corresponding saturated vapor pressures being P and $P + dP$. Draw two adiabatic curves passing through the points A and B. They intersect the other isothermal curve at A' and B'. Since the two isothermals are very close to each other, the points A', B' are very close to the end points of the horizontal section. The cycle $ABB'A'A$ thus forms a Carnot cycle,

63

and we may apply the Carnot theorem,

$$\frac{dW}{Q} = \frac{dT}{T},\qquad(48)$$

where dW is the work performed in the reversible cycle and Q is the heat absorbed in the isothermal process at temperature $T + dT$. For one gram of working substance, Q equals the latent heat of evaporation* and dW equals the area enclosed by the loop $ABB'A'A$ which equals $dP(V_2 - V_1)$, where V_2 and V_1 are the specific volumes of the vapor and the liquid. Hence,

$$\frac{dP(V_2 - V_1)}{L} = \frac{dT}{T}.\qquad(49)$$

In other words,

$$\frac{dP}{dT} = \frac{L}{T(V_2 - V_1)}.\qquad(50)$$

The right-hand side consists of known quantities. Thus, the rate of increase of the boiling point T with respect to the increase of pressure P may be calculated theoretically and compared with experimental results. The above equation is known as the *Clausius-Clapeyron equation*; it has been verified by experiment.

The second application is concerned with the reversible cell. Take the Daniell cell as an example. It consists of a Cu electrode dipped in a $CuSO_4$ solution and a Zn electrode dipped in a $ZnSO_4$ solution, the two solutions being separated by a porous partition. The cell maintains a *constant* electromotive force of 1.096 volts during discharge, the electrical energy being supplied by the energy released in the chemical reaction plus the heat absorbed from the surroundings. Thus the Daniell cell is a thermodynamic system,

---

* In thermodynamics we are interested only in the absorption of heat and the performance of work of a system, disregarding the mechanisms involved. Thus the absorption of heat by a perfect gas, the absorption of latent heat in the present problem, and the absorption of heat by an electric cell in the next are treated on an equal basis in spite of the fact that the three mechanisms involved are completely different. The same applies to the work performed. This discussion also brings out the generality of thermodynamics, an advantage over the theories based on the detailed mechanisms.

not a purely mechanical system; the emf and charge are thermo-dynamic variables, not purely mechanical variables. The chemical reaction that takes place inside is represented by the following equation:

$$Zn + CuSO_4 \rightleftharpoons Cu + ZnSO_4 + 50{,}130 \text{ cal.} \qquad (51)$$

When this reaction takes place in a test tube, it is a spontaneous process and is not reversible. However, the physical arrangement of the Daniell cell makes it possible to carry out this reaction reversibly (just as the use of the semipermeable membranes makes it possible to carry out the diffusion process reversibly). Suppose we connect the two electrodes to a capacitor of an extremely large capacitance charged to a voltage of 1.096 volts in a direction against the emf of the cell. No current will flow in the circuit; no chemical reaction will take place inside (microscopically the Cu electrode has a voltage which prevents the deposit of further Cu ions on it). The whole system is in mechanical equilibrium. Now let an infinitesimal external influence be applied to the capacitor. For example, the two plates may be moved slightly closer to each other so as to make the voltage slightly lower than 1.096 volts; as a result, a current begins to flow in the circuit tending to charge the capacitor. At the same time a chemical reaction takes place inside the cell. The work performed by the cell is stored in the capacitor. Since the emf of the cell is always 1.096 volts in dis-charging and the voltage of the capacitor does not increase in charging (due to the extremely large capacitance), the equilibrium between the cell and the capacitor (acting as a "weight") is always maintained (disregarding the infinitesimal change) as the current flows. The cell changes from one equilibrium state to another as the current flows; the independent variable of the interaction is the amount of charge q entering the capacitor (or the amount of Cu deposited, the two being one-to-one related as one Cu ion deposited on the electrode contributes two electronic units of positive charge). Furthermore, by reversing the direction of the infinitesi-mal external influence (increasing the distance separating the two plates) the process may be made to proceed in the reversed

65

direction. Thus, the sequence of equilibrium states forms a reversible process.

If the cell were to involve only the chemical effect and the electric effect it would be a purely mechanical system in neutral equilibrium. The cell is a thermodynamic system and the process is a reversible process because it also has a thermal effect, i.e., the cell absorbs heat from the surroundings during the discharge process and releases the same amount of heat in the reversed process—the charge process. In so doing, the cell may serve the same purpose as any working substance in a heat engine, and the Carnot theorem may be applied. We construct a Carnot cycle by the following four steps: (1), an isothermal process by which an amount of heat H is absorbed by the cell during discharging at temperature T; (2), an adiabatic process by which the temperature of the cell is lowered by an amount dT; (3), an isothermal process by which the cell is recharged at the lower temperature and thus, at a different emf;* (4), an adiabatic process by which the temperature is brought back to the original value. As mentioned before, in the isothermal process the independent variable of the mechanical interaction is the amount of charge q passed through the circuit. Thus, q plays the same role as the volume V of a gas. Since the mechanical equilibrium is achieved by the equality of the emf of the cell E and the voltage of the capacitor, the variable E plays the same role as the pressure P of a gas. Therefore, q and E are the independent thermodynamic variables of the cell just as P and V are for a gas. There are no other independent variables because the only mechanical interaction possessed by the cell is the electric interaction. The Carnot cycle may be represented by a rectangular loop in the E-q diagram as shown in Fig. 5. The work performed in one cycle of operation is again represented by the area of the loop,

$$dW = q_0 \, dE. \tag{52}$$

The Carnot theorem thus leads to the following relation:

$$\frac{q_0 \, dE}{H} = \frac{dT}{T}. \tag{53}$$

* The emf of a reversible cell is dependent on temperature.

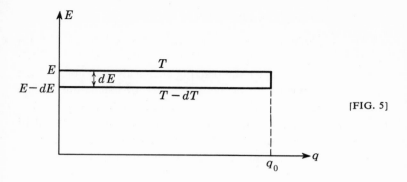

[FIG. 5]

In other words,

$$H = q_0 T \frac{dE}{dT}.$$ (54)

The total electrical energy obtained in discharge equals the heat H absorbed plus the energy of chemical reaction which is also proportional to q_0, i.e.,

$$q_0 E = H + q_0 U_r$$ (55)

where U_r is the heat of reaction per unit charge. Combining the above two equations we derive the following:

$$E - T \frac{dE}{dT} = U_r.$$ (56)

This equation gives the temperature dependence of the emf of a reversible cell. It is known as the *Gibbs-Helmholtz equation*.

The two examples given above have been worked out by using the Carnot theorem deduced in the previous section. However, they may be solved in a simpler manner by making use of the thermodynamical relations which we omit. The Clausius-Clapeyron equation may be deduced from a Maxwell relation and the Gibbs-Helmholtz equation may be deduced from a thermodynamical relation involving a thermodynamic function called free energy. The two examples also demonstrate the power of the thermodynamical method, by which it is possible to treat such diverse systems as the imperfect gas and the electrical cell within the same theoretical framework.

67

3. Chemical applications

Chemical equilibrium is perhaps the best example of thermo-dynamical equilibrium because all three types of interaction take place at the same time—the reacting chemicals may absorb heat from the surroundings and perform work by expanding against the surroundings; also, the reactants and products may diffuse with respect to each other to form a uniform mixture. We shall discuss one simple example—the law of mass action for isothermal-isochoric reactions (reactions of gases kept at a constant volume).

Consider a mixture of nitrogen and hydrogen. Under proper conditions some of the nitrogen and hydrogen may combine to form ammonia gas. The chemical reaction is represented by

$$N_2 + 3H_2 \rightleftharpoons 2NH_3 + Q_r \qquad (57)$$

where Q_r is the heat of reaction. Thus, starting from the mixture of the two gases, a spontaneous process takes place in which ammonia is formed until the amount of ammonia has reached a certain value and an equilibrium is established among nitrogen, hydrogen, and ammonia. Here the spontaneous process takes place among three components not separated by walls, but mixed together. This does not prevent us from treating the process on the same basis as one in which the components are separated by walls. The mixture is a composite system specified by a number of thermodynamic variables among which are the molar numbers of the separate gases. As the spontaneous process proceeds, these variables change in a specified direction until equilibrium is established. The independent variable of the interaction is the amount dm of ammonia created. Since the amount of ammonia created is definitely related to the amounts of nitrogen and hydrogen consumed by the chemical equation, the latter may also be used as the independent variable. In thermodynamics we do not consider the physical mechanism of the constraints; we only consider the thermodynamical consequences once the independent variable dm is allowed to vary by removing the constraints. In chemical reactions this is usually achieved by the introduction of catalysts. As the spontaneous process proceeds, the thermo-dynamic state of the composite system changes through a sequence of states, each of which could be an equilibrium state when the constraints are imposed again, that is, when the catalyst is removed. Each state is specified by a definite composition of the mixture and thus has a definite value of entropy. Now we have a sequence of states mutually accessible by varying the independent variable dm. Our basic assumption (the law of spontaneous processes) thus *demands* (1) that a spontaneous process take place leading from one state to another in a sequence in which the entropy increases, and (2) that the process reach an equilibrium at which the entropy is a maximum with respect to dm. Once we know the reaction is possible, these assertions follow in our theory and the predictions may be compared with the experimental results to test the validity of our assumption.

The type of chemical reaction discussed above does not repre-sent a new, independent spontaneous process in addition to the three types discussed before. In this respect we may note that in the preceding chapter the diffusive process is treated as an independent process. The entropy of a mixture is not *defined* in the discussion of thermal and mechanical processes, but is *defined* in the diffusive interaction by a reversible process. Therefore the increase of entropy must be *verified* for this extension of the definition of entropy to mixtures, as we did in Chapter 3, Section 3 (F); it is not *demanded* by the basic assumption. In the present case the entropy for the sequence of states involved is already defined and therefore its increase is demanded by the basic assumption. The comparison with experimental results will either prove or disprove the basic assumption.

To see how a chemical reaction may be regarded as a combina-tion of the three types of interaction discussed above, we first consider a reversible process by which the reactants are converted into the products. Suppose we have a reaction chamber (Fig. 6) in which the three gases, N_2, H_2, and NH_3, are in chemical equilib-rium at temperature T. Their partial pressures are denoted by

69

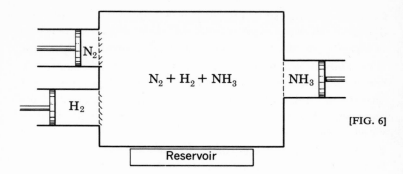

[FIG. 6]

P_N, P_H, and P_A. Let one side of the chamber be provided with two windows covered by semipermeable membranes permeable only to N_2 and H_2, respectively, and the other side, a window with a membrane permeable only to NH_3. The three windows are connected to three cylinders provided with frictionless pistons; the cylinders contain the three gases, respectively, their pressures being equal to the respective partial pressures in the reaction chamber so as to maintain diffusive equilibrium. Now apply a slight pressure on the pistons of the N_2 and H_2 gases such that for every one mole of N_2 entering the reaction chamber, three moles of H_2 enter at the same time. Also apply a slight negative pressure on the piston of NH_3 gas. As a result, two moles of NH_3 will come out of the chamber for every one mole of N_2 and three moles of H_2 added to it. Since the reaction evolves heat, the heat of reaction U_r must be removed reversibly by a reservoir so that the chamber is maintained at the same temperature T. The above setup provides a reversible process by which a volume of one mole of N_2 at the state (T, P_N) and another volume of three moles of H_2 at the state (T, P_H) are converted into a volume of two moles of NH_3 at the state (T, P_A); at the same time the reservoir absorbs an amount of heat Q_r at temperature T. This process involves a thermal interaction and a mechanical interaction (heat exchanged with the reservoir and work performed by the gases when the volumes change), as does the conversion of one gram of water to one gram of steam, in which heat is exchanged and work is performed. The

70

change of the chemical property of the system does not concern us in thermodynamics, just as the change of the physical property from liquid to gas does not concern us in the latter case.

With this reversible process the spontaneous process of a mixture of N_2 and H_2 reacting to reach an equilibrium may be analyzed and regarded as a combination of a series of processes of the three basic types. Suppose the mixture starts with a volume V and partial pressures of N_2 and H_2 equal $P_N{}^0$ and $P_H{}^0$, there being no NH_3. The equilibrium partial pressures are again denoted by P_N, P_H, and P_A. Since some N_2 and H_2 must have been consumed to create NH_3 in the equilibrium state, we conclude, keeping in mind the isothermal-isochoric condition, that

$$P_N < P_N{}^0, \quad P_H < P_H{}^0. \tag{58}$$

The final state of equilibrium may be reached by the following sequence: (1) A diffusive reversible process separating the initial mixture into two separate gases—N_2 in the state $(P_N{}^0, V)$ and H_2 in the state $(P_H{}^0, V)$. (2) An irreversible process of expansion against vacuum by which N_2 changes from $(P_N{}^0, V)$ to $(P_N, V_N{}')$ and a similar process by which H_2 changes from $(P_H{}^0, V)$ to $(P_H, V_H{}')$. Both volumes increase because both pressures decrease,

$$V_N{}' > V, \quad V_H{}' > V. \tag{59}$$

(3) Connect the two volumes to the two left windows of the reaction chamber inside which the partial pressures are P_N, P_H, and P_A so that a reversible process may take place by which a volume $V_N{}' - V$ of N_2 and a volume of $V_H{}' - V$ of H_2 combine to form a volume V of NH_3 in the right cylinder. The amounts of H_2 and N_2 must combine exactly to form NH_3 with no leftovers, because in the final state of the spontaneous process there exists a volume V of H_2 at pressure P_H and a volume V of N_2 at pressure P_N, the rest being combined exactly to form NH_3. Furthermore, the NH_3 formed in the right cylinder must have a volume exactly equal to V because of the following: Since its temperature T and pressure P_A

are the same as those of the NH_3 in the final state of the spontaneous process, so must be the volume, which in the latter case is V.
(4) Finally, a reversible diffusive process by which the gases remaining in the cylinders, i.e., N_2 at (V, P_N, T), H_2 at (V, P_H, T) and NH_3 at (V, P_A, T) are telescoped into a mixture of volume V, pressure $P_N + P_H + P_A$, and temperature T, which is the final state of the spontaneous process. The four processes are all of the three basic types; thus the chemical reaction is analyzed as a combination of the three basic interactions.

In the four processes, three are reversible, in which entropy does not change, and one is irreversible (the second), in which the total entropy increases. Thus the entropy increases in the chemical reaction, as all spontaneous processes should.

Having discussed the conceptual side of the problem, we now return to the application of the equilibrium condition $dS = 0$ to deduce the relation of the partial pressures of the gases in equilibrium, i.e., to *derive* the law of mass action. In general we consider a chemical reaction specified by

$$aA + bB + cC + \cdots \rightleftharpoons lL + mM + nN + \cdots + Q_r \quad (60)$$

where $A, B, C, \ldots$, are reactants, $L, M, N, \ldots$, are products, all assumed to be ideal gases, $a, b, c, \ldots l, m, n, \ldots$, are the numbers of molecules, and Q_r is the heat evolved in the reaction. The reaction is isothermal-isochoric, the heat of reaction being removed by a reservoir (the surroundings) and the volume of the mixture being kept constant. The composite system concerned consists of the mixture of gases and the surroundings. By the additivity of entropy and by separating the mixture into individual gases by semipermeable membranes we find the total entropy of the composite system to be

$$S = n_a S_a + n_b S_b + \cdots + n_l S_l + n_m S_m + \cdots + S_s \quad (61)$$

where $S_a, S_b, \ldots, S_l, S_m, \ldots$ are the entropy per mole of the gases $A, B, \ldots, L, M, \ldots$, respectively, calculated at the same temperature and partial pressures of the mixture, $n_a, n_b, \ldots, n_l, n_m, \ldots$, are the respective molar numbers, and S_s is the entropy of the surroundings. In equilibrium the change of the total entropy dS due to a change of the independent variable of the interaction dm must be zero. Take the change of mass of A as dm and let $dm = -a$ moles. The corresponding changes of masses of B, C, ... , L, M, N, ... are $-b$, $-c$, ... , l, m, n, ... moles, respectively. The corresponding change of dS is due to the appearance of l moles of L, m moles of M, ... , the disappearance of a moles of A, b moles of B, ... , and the absorption of heat Q_r by the surroundings at temperature T. Thus

$$dS = -aS_a - bS_b - cS_c - \cdots + lS_l + mS_m$$
$$+ nS_n + \cdots + \frac{U_r}{T} = 0. \quad (62)$$

The entropy of n moles of perfect gas has been calculated at the end of Section 3, Chapter 3. The result is

$$S = n(C_P \ln T - R \ln P + k). \quad (63)$$

For the purpose of calculation in the isothermal-isochoric processes we change the variable P to the variable V. Also replace k by $R \ln i$, where i is another constant. Thus,

$$S = n\left(C_P \ln T - R \ln \frac{nRT}{V} + R \ln i\right). \quad (64)$$

$$= n\left(C_V \ln T - R \ln \frac{nR}{V} + R \ln i\right). \quad (65)$$

The equilibrium condition $dS = 0$ thus leads to the following equation:

$$- a\left(C_{V_a} \ln T - R \ln \frac{n_a R}{V} + R \ln i_a\right)$$

$$- b\left(C_{V_b} \ln T - R \ln \frac{n_b R}{V} + R \ln i_b\right) - \cdots$$

$$+ l\left(C_{V_l} \ln T - R \ln \frac{n_l R}{V} + R \ln i_l\right)$$

$$+ m\left(C_{V_m} \ln T - R \ln \frac{n_m R}{V} + R \ln i_m\right) + \cdots + \frac{U_r}{T} = 0. \quad (66)$$

73

The above equation may be rearranged as follows

$$(-aC_{V_a} - bC_{V_b} - \cdots + lC_{V_l} + mC_{V_m} + \cdots)\frac{\ln T}{R}$$

$$- (-a - b - \cdots + l + m + \cdots)\ln\frac{R}{V}$$

$$+ \ln\frac{i_l^{\,l}i_m^{\,m}\cdots}{i_a^{\,a}i_b^{\,b}\cdots} + \frac{Ur}{RT} = -\ln\frac{n_a^{\,a}n_b^{\,b}\cdots}{n_l^{\,l}n_m^{\,m}\cdots}. \quad (67)$$

Let the left-hand side of this equation be denoted by $\ln K_x$, which depends only on T, V, and the characteristics of the gases involved. Thus we have

$$\frac{n_l^{\,l}n_m^{\,m}\cdots}{n_a^{\,a}n_b^{\,b}\cdots} = K_x. \quad (68)$$

The right-hand side is a constant for a fixed temperature and a fixed volume. The above equation expresses the relation among the equilibrium concentrations of gases A, B, $\ldots$, L, M, $\ldots$. This equation is the mathematical expression of the law of mass action. Thus we have deduced the law theoretically from the law of spontaneous processes. Furthermore, we have the theoretical expression of the equilibrium constant K_x and are able to predict the change of the equilibrium due to a change of temperature or volume. The derivation of the law of mass action by the kinetic theory of gases (a microscopic theory) is well known; nevertheless the expression of the equilibrium constant cannot be derived.

V

THE MICROSCOPIC INTERPRETATION
OF THERMODYNAMICS

Thermodynamics is a macroscopic theory. It deals with phenomena directly observable on a large scale. From the experimental facts we formulate the basic laws by induction. The basic laws are then developed mathematically, and may be applied to solve practical problems. As far as a macroscopic theory of equilibrium is concerned, thermodynamics (including the third law which we do not discuss) has been developed to such a state of perfection that no more drastic new discovery is expected.

The macroscopic theory tells us *how* the physical universe behaves, but not *why*. The basic laws are taken as axioms, not deductible from other principles. The characteristics of a particular material system are specified by a set of physical constants, the values of which are made known to us by experimental investigation, not by theoretical derivation. Furthermore, the basic laws and the physical constants of different fields of investigation seem to be independent of one another. Thus, the complete description of the whole physical universe is provided by a large number of independent laws and a large body of unrelated physical constants. If this is all we know, the physical behavior of the universe is very complicated indeed.

Is it possible that the various laws and the numerous constants may be explained and expressed in terms of a few fundamental laws and constants? The belief that it is possible is one of the driving forces in the theoretical development of science. This possibility is supported by the experimental fact that some correlations between the laws and the constants do exist. For example, the electrical conductivity and the heat conductivity are related by the *Wiedemann-Franz law*. Evidently electrical conductivity and heat conductivity are not independent of each other and both may be the manifestation of some physical entity* that is not directly observable but plays a more fundamental role.

The attempt to reduce the behavior of the physical universe to a few simple, fundamental laws is as old as science itself. We do not intend to trace the development of this school of thought. We shall only say that this approach has succeeded remarkably well in the modern atomic theory. In this theory, all the macroscopic phenomena of the physical world are interpretable in terms of the properties of the atoms and the interactions among them. In the sense that the atomic theory explains the macroscopic phenomena in terms of an entity (the atom) outside the realm of the macroscopic theory, we may say that it answers not only how nature behaves, but also why. Of course, explanation is but a sequence of deduction, and in the end of this sequence there is always something taken as the axiom which in turn is unexplained. Yet the atomic theory does simplify the behavior of the physical world tremendously and does provide an understanding of natural phenomena on a deeper level than is obtainable from the macroscopic theories.

Once we have a successful atomic theory we can no longer be satisfied with the laws and constants of a macroscopic theory. We are not satisfied with simply knowing the laws of heat conduction and electrical conduction; we also want to derive them from the atomic theory of matter. We are no longer satisfied with determining electrical conductivity and heat conductivity by experiment; we also want to calculate their values theoretically in terms

---

* That is, the free electrons of the conductor, according to the atomic theory.

of the atomic constants. The Wiedemann-Franz law is also expected to be deduced from the atomic theory. Likewise, in thermodynamics we want an explanation of the basic laws discussed in the previous chapters in terms of the behavior of the atom; we also want the macroscopic quantities introduced (temperature, heat, and entropy) to be expressed in terms of atomic quantities. These objectives are fulfilled in the microscopic theories of heat, which consist of the kinetic theory of gases and statistical mechanics.

The interpretation of thermodynamics by microscopic theory is well known and no attempt is made to develop it systematically here. The purpose of this chapter is to show that the three basic macroscopic laws and the three basic macroscopic quantities may be explained in terms of the atomic theory more naturally in the present formulation of thermodynamics.

1. Interpretation of the first law of thermodynamics*

In the macroscopic theory, heat is a quantity outside mechanics. Its existence is established empirically. The equivalence of heat and mechanical work is ascertained by experiments. On this basis we establish the first law of thermodynamics.

In the atomic theory the heat energy of a substance is identified with the total mechanical energies of the molecules of the substance. Thus, the quantity of heat is reduced to a mechanical concept on the microscopic level. The first law of thermodynamics thus becomes the mechanical law of conservation of energy applied to molecules, which follows directly from mechanics and need not be introduced separately.

The macroscopic quantity of internal energy may now be expressed in terms of atomic quantities and assigned an absolute value; it is the sum of all the energies of the molecules of a thermodynamic system.

* The zeroth law will be discussed after the first and the second.

2. Interpretation of the second law of thermodynamics

We have mentioned before that attempts to explain the second law in terms of mechanics were not successful. Entropy is not a mechanical quantity. According to the atomic theory, a thermodynamic system is a mechanical system consisting of a large number of similar particles. The following question thus arises: how can the second law (and entropy) find a place in such a mechanical system?

A clue leading to the answer to this question may be found in the fact that the mechanical system we are considering is one consisting of a large number of similar particles. Since the number is large it is hopeless to trace out the exact mechanical behavior of all the particles, but since the particles are similar there is hope that they may be treated on a statistical basis; here a new element enters—the law of probability. The relation between the second law and the probability law may be brought out by first considering the following analogy.

When we flip a coin there are two possible results, heads or tails. When we flip a hundred coins there are a large number of possible results, the numbers of heads and tails could be (100, 0) or (99, 1) or (98, 2) . . . or (0, 100). Each possible result (n_1, n_2) we call a *configuration*. In an actual flipping, it is obvious that the configuration (100, 0) and (0, 100) are seldom realized and the most likely result is (50, 50). The reason is that there is only one *combination* of the positions of the coins leading to the configuration (100, 0) or (0, 100), i.e., all heads up or all tails up; whereas there are many combinations leading to the (50, 50) configuration. Thus in the (50, 50) configuration when we change one coin from head to tail and another from tail to head we get a new combination, but the configuration remains the same. All possible combinations of the (50, 50) configuration may be generated this way, and they are numerous. If all the combinations of the positions of the coins have equal probability to occur in the flipping, then the probability for the (50, 50) configuration to

78

occur is much greater than that of the (100, 0) configuration. If we have one hundred coins starting with the (100, 0) configuration and we keep flipping them in a random fashion, we may expect from the probability law that the configuration changes in time from (100, 0) to others of larger probability until finally it has changed to the configuration with the largest probability, i.e., (50, 50). Once the maximum is arrived at, the configuration changes no more except for the fluctuations. Incidentally, the change of the configuration takes place in a specified direction—n_1 decreases monotonically* and n_2 increases monotonically, there being no oscillations.

The similarity of the change of configurations in coin flipping and the change of thermodynamic states in spontaneous processes is obvious. Both proceed spontaneously, change monotonically, and reach equilibrium eventually. Thus, it may well be that the spontaneous process is in principle similar to the flipping of coins, and is governed by the same law of probability.

That this is actually so is established by the atomic theory. In this theory a gas is regarded as a large collection of molecules, each moving with a certain velocity. The positions of the molecules change by motion and the velocities of the molecules change by collisions, but the thermodynamic state of the gas remains unchanged. Thus, the thermodynamic state (*macroscopic state*) may be compared to the *configuration* in coin flipping and the thermodynamic variables P, V, T correspond to the numbers n_1 and n_2 (the variable T is independent just as n_2 is independent). The molecular state of motion of a gas (*microscopic state*) specified by the positions and velocities of all molecules may be compared to the *combination* in coin flipping. Each macroscopic state corresponds to a large number of microscopic states. If each microscopic state is assigned equal probability (this is the basic assumption in statistical mechanics) then the macroscopic state with a large number of microscopic states will have a large probability of occurring. The spontaneous process may be compared

---

* Disregarding fluctuation, which becomes less significant when the number of particles becomes very large.

to the continual random flipping of the coins starting with an arbitrary configuration. The interaction of the process may be compared to the act of flipping which allows one microscopic state to change to another. The constraints of the spontaneous process are the factors that prevent the microscopic state from changing to a set of specified microscopic states. When an interaction is introduced, the microscopic state is allowed to change within the limitation of the remaining constraints and the law of probability demands that the macroscopic state change from one of small probability to one of large probability accessible by the interaction, and the change will not stop until the probability has reached a maximum* with respect to all accessible states. This prediction of the microscopic theory is verified by the macroscopic law of spontaneous processes. Therefore, the second law may be interpreted as the manifestation of the probability law when applied to a system of a large number of molecules. The potential of spontaneous transition (entropy) is thus interpreted as a quantity related to the probability, the maximum of entropy corresponding to the maximum of probability. Thus, we have explained the second law and entropy in terms of microscopic theory.

We may return to the spontaneous process of the free expansion of a gas (against vacuum). The initial state has a volume V. The final state has a volume $V + V'$. Before the expansion, the volume V' is not available to the molecules. The microscopic states with molecules in volume V' are not accessible because of the constraint —the partition. Once the partition is removed they become accessible. Once molecules are in V' it is very unlikely that by chance they should all move back to volume V, leaving volume V' a vacuum again. Thus, the spontaneous process proceeds in such a way that molecules move from the volume V to V' until both are equally occupied.†

* Again we disregard fluctuation. Thus the macroscopic theory (thermodynamics) deals with the gross feature only. The fine feature (fluctuation) is to be dealt with in the microscopic theory (statistical mechanics).

† The two volumes V and V' may be compared to the two sides of a coin and the expansion may be compared to the change from (100, 0) to (50, 50).

We have not completely established the relation between entropy and probability. The *thermodynamical probability* is a quantity that needs careful definition; we do not intend to discuss the fine points here. (The probability may be defined more naturally in the quantum theory which makes an actual *counting* of the microscopic states possible.) Nevertheless, one fact is certain. When we deal with composite systems, probability is a multiplicative quantity, but entropy is an additive quantity. If the probability W is related to the entropy S by a function f,

$$S = f(W), \tag{69}$$

this function must satisfy the following equation stating that entropy is additive:

$$f(W_1 \cdot W_2) = f(W_1) + f(W_2). \tag{70}$$

This functional relation may be solved, and the general solution is as follows:

$$f(W) = k \ln W + C \tag{71}$$

where k and C are two constants. Boltzmann deduced the above equation, but left the two constants undetermined. Planck replaced W by the number of combinations P of a given configuration, which is proportional to W, and also assumed the additive constant to be zero. Thus

$$S = k \ln P. \tag{72}$$

The constant k may be identified by applying the above relation to an actual thermodynamic system, e.g., the perfect gas. The change of entropy of n moles of perfect gas in a free expansion from volume V_1 to volume V_2 is

$$S_2 - S_1 = nR \ln V_2 - nR \ln V_1. \tag{73}$$

Thus

$$k \ln \left(\frac{P_2}{P_1} \right) = nR \ln \frac{V_2}{V_1}. \tag{74}$$

The probability for one molecule to be found in a volume V_1 is proportional to V_1; in volume V_2, proportional to V_2. The probability for all N molecules to be found in V_1 is proportional to $V_1{}^N$; in V_2 proportional to $V_2{}^N$. Therefore, P_2/P_1 equals $(V_2/V_1)^N$.* The above equation thus results in

$$kN = nR. \qquad (75)$$

Therefore, the constant k equals the universal gas constant divided by the Avogadro number. This constant is called the *Boltzmann constant*.

The statistical interpretation assigns a meaning to the absolute value of entropy, while in the macroscopic theory only the change of entropy has a physical significance. Thus, the theory is carried one step further, which would not be possible if it remained macroscopic.

A number of results obtained in Chapter 3 may be interpreted easily on the statistical basis. In the adiabatic reversible process the entropy of the "weight" does not change. This result may be looked upon from the microscopic theory as follows: When a weight gains an amount of gravitational energy E, say, in an adiabatic reversible process, each molecule of it gains the same amount of gravitational energy because the weight has undergone a translational motion. In general, an amount of energy gain E might be distributed among the molecules in a large number of combinations. But, in the case of gravitational energy, there is only one combination, that is, all molecules gain the same amount. The number of microscopic states is thus 1. Since $\ln 1 = 0$ the entropy change is zero. In the dissipative process the kinetic energy of the wheel is converted into internal energy of the fluid. When the amount of energy takes the form of kinetic energy of rotation of the wheel, there is only one way the energy may be distributed among the molecules—all of them must move with the same angular velocity (the same linear velocity for the translational energy of a weight). When it takes the form of molecular energies of the fluid there are a large number of combinations.

* In this example we have the advantage of the fact that the volume is the only thermodynamic variable that changes. This simplifies the calculation of probability, and we are able to deduce significant results without an exhaustive discussion of the microscopic states and the thermodynamical probability.

The spontaneous process proceeds from a macroscopic state with small number of microscopic states to one of large number, in agreement with the macroscopic observation. The increase of entropy in the dissipative process is thus explained.

The above results may also be stated by saying that increase of entropy is associated to the increase of randomness of the molecules.

3. Interpretation of the zeroth law of thermodynamics

In concluding our study of thermodynamics, we return to our starting point—the zeroth law of thermodynamics. The concept of temperature with its characteristic property specified by the zeroth law is outside of mechanics. In the atomic theory, a thermodynamic system is regarded as a mechanical system of a large number of molecules. The question thus arises: how can the zeroth law and thus the temperature concept find a place in such a mechanical system?

Let us first consider a related problem—the energy distribution of the molecules in a thermodynamic system. Suppose in a system a molecule can take on the energy values $E_1, E_2, \ldots, E_i, \ldots, E_s$. (In the classical theory these values usually form a continuous spectrum from zero to infinity. However, in the quantum theory they form a discrete spectrum because all thermodynamic systems of interest are bound systems.) Out of the total N molecules of the system, some may have energy E_1, some E_2, etc. Let the respective numbers of molecules for the various energies be $N_1, N_2, \ldots, N_i, \ldots, N_s$. A distribution specified by a set of numbers ($N_1, N_2, \ldots, N_i, \ldots$) represents a configuration. When we exchange two molecules of different energies, the *combination* of the molecules changes, but the *configuration* does not change. (Here we assume that the molecules are distinguishable.) The total number of combinations for this configuration is

$$\frac{N!}{N_1! \, N_2! \cdots N_i! \cdots} . \tag{76}$$

Now a given amount of energy E may be distributed among the N molecules in a number of configurations. The *thermodynamical probability* W for a given configuration to occur is the number of combinations of this configuration divided by the total number of combinations possible, which is S^N. Thus

$$W = \frac{N!}{N_1! \, N_2! \cdots N_i! \cdots} \frac{1}{s^N} \tag{77}$$

According to the statistical principle the configuration actually realized is the one having the maximum thermodynamical probability. Therefore, the energy distribution of molecules $(N_1, N_2, \ldots, N_i, \ldots)$ may be determined by finding the configuration which makes W a maximum. Since the maximum of W is also the maximum of $\ln W$ we determine the latter for mathematical convenience. The maximum condition is thus

$$d(\ln W) = -\sum_i d \ln N_i! = 0. \tag{78}$$

To evaluate $\ln N_i!$ we make use of a mathematical theorem expressed by the so-called Stirling formula

$$\ln X! = X \ln X - X, \tag{79}$$

which is a good approximation for large values of X. The maximum condition then becomes

$$\sum_i d(N_i \ln N_i - N_i) = 0, \tag{80}$$

or

$$\sum_i \ln N_i \, dN_i = 0. \tag{81}$$

The differentials $dN_1, dN_2, \ldots dN_i, \ldots$, are not completely independent of one another because the N_i's must be such that the total number of molecules be a constant N and the total energy of the molecules be a constant E,

$$\sum_i N_i = N, \tag{82}$$

$$\sum_i E_i N_i = E. \tag{83}$$

84

Therefore,

$$\sum_i dN_i = 0, \tag{84}$$

$$\sum_i E_i \, dN_i = 0. \tag{85}$$

These are the conditions the differentials dN_i must satisfy. Thus two of the dN_i's are not independent and may be expressed in terms of the other dN_i's by solving the above two equations. With the two dependent dN_i's eliminated in Eq. (81) the remaining dN_i's are independent of one another and their coefficients must all be zero to satisfy Eq. (81). The result of this calculation may also be obtained more simply by the method of Lagrange's multiplier. Multiply Eq. (84) by a constant λ and Eq. (85) by a constant μ and add the two equations to Eq. (90); we get

$$\sum_i (\ln N_i + \lambda + \mu E_i) \, dN_i = 0. \tag{86}$$

It can be proved mathematically that the result we desired may be obtained by setting the coefficients of *all* dN_i's in the above equation equal to zero and then eliminating the constants λ and μ in terms of N and E. Thus we obtain a series of equations

$$\ln N_i + \lambda + \mu E_i = 0, \qquad i = 1, 2, \ldots, s. \tag{87}$$

The solutions of them are

$$N_i = e^{-\lambda - \mu E_i}, \qquad i = 1, 2, \ldots, s. \tag{88}$$

Introducing another constant $A = e^{-\lambda}$ we have

$$N_i = A e^{-\mu E_i}, \qquad i = 1, 2, \ldots, s. \tag{89}$$

The constants A and μ are to be determined by the following conditions:

$$\sum_i N_i = \sum_i A e^{-\mu E_i} = N, \tag{90}$$

$$\sum_i E_i N_i = \sum_i A E_i e^{-\mu E_i} = E. \tag{91}$$

Thus we have deduced the energy distribution function representing N_i as a function of the energy E_i for all values of i. This

85

distribution function is known as the *Maxwell-Boltzmann distribution function* and is valid for a system of distinguishable molecules. Incidentally the average energy per molecule E/N, as may be seen from the last two equations, depends only on the constant μ, not on A. Furthermore, the average energy per molecule is proportional to $1/\mu$ as $1/\mu$ has the dimension of energy. It can be proved, though we omit the proof here, that *the average energy per degree of freedom of a molecule equals* $1/2\mu$.

We now return to the problem of two thermodynamic systems interacting thermally with each other. The energy of one system may be distributed over the molecules in a number of configurations $(N_1, N_2, \ldots, N_s)$. The energy of the other system may also be distributed over the molecules in a number of configurations $(N_1', N_2', \ldots, N_t')$. The configuration of the composite system is thus specified by $(N_1, N_2, \ldots, N_s; N_1', N_2', \ldots, N_t')$. The probability of a configuration of the composite system is thus

$$W = \frac{N!\,N'!}{N_1!\,N_2! \cdots N_i! \cdots N_1'!\,N_2'! \cdots N_i'! \cdots} \frac{1}{s^{N}t^{N'}}. \quad (92)$$

If the two systems were completely separated from each other, then the values N_i and N_i' would each satisfy two conditions of the form of Eqs. (82) and (83) and we would have a total of *four* conditions. When the two systems are allowed to interact thermally, the total energy of the molecules of one system need not be constant; only the total energy of the composite systems need be constant. Thus, the values N_i and N_i' satisfy the following *three* conditions:

$$\sum_i N_i = N, \quad (93)$$

$$\sum_i N_i' = N', \quad (94)$$

$$\sum_i E_i N_i + \sum_i E_i' N_i' = E. \quad (95)$$

The introduction of the interaction thus removes one constraint equation. Within the remaining constraints (the above three equations) the composite system may assume a number of

86

possible configurations, each corresponding to a particular division of energy E between the two systems. If the composite system starts with a configuration with a value of W not equal to the maximum of the possible configurations, then the law of probability demands that the configuration change gradually until it has changed to the configuration of maximum probability. This explains the change described in the second law of thermodynamics; it also tells us that the state of thermal equilibrium is represented by the configuration of the composite system which has a maximum value of W under the constraints of the above three equations. To determine this configuration we proceed in exactly the same manner as before. Thus

$$\sum_i d(\ln N_i! + \ln N_i'!) = 0, \qquad (96)$$

$$\sum_i d(N_i \ln N_i - N_i + N_i' \ln N_i' - N_i') = 0, \qquad (97)$$

$$\sum_i (\ln N_i \, dN_i + \ln N_i' \, dN_i') = 0. \qquad (98)$$

From the constraint equations we get

$$\sum_i dN_i = 0, \qquad (99)$$

$$\sum_i dN_i' = 0, \qquad (100)$$

$$\sum_i (E_i \, dN_i + E_i' \, dN_i') = 0. \qquad (101)$$

By the method of Lagrange's multiplier, we obtain

$$\sum_i (\ln N_i + \lambda + \mu E_i) \, dN_i + \sum_i (\ln N_i' + \lambda' + \mu E_i') \, dN_i' = 0. \qquad (102)$$

Thus

$$N_i = e^{-\lambda - \mu E_i}, \qquad i = 1, 2, \ldots, s; \qquad (103)$$

$$N_i' = e^{-\lambda' - \mu E_i'}, \qquad i = 1, 2, \ldots, t. \qquad (104)$$

Notice that only three multipliers, λ, λ', and μ, appear, there being no μ' because we have only one equation constraining the total energy. Introducing constants A and A' in a similar manner we rewrite the above two equations as follows:

$$N_i = Ae^{-\mu E_i}, \qquad i = 1, 2, \ldots, s; \tag{105}$$

$$N_i' = A'e^{-\mu E_i'}, \qquad i = 1, 2, \ldots, t. \tag{106}$$

The constants A, A', and μ are to be determined by the constants N, N', and E. The equilibrium configuration given above shows that both systems obey the Maxwell-Boltzmann distribution separately. More importantly, the parameter μ of the distribution is the same for the two systems. In the macroscopic theory, systems in thermal equilibrium are characterized by equal temperature. In the microscopic theory, systems in thermal equilibrium are characterized by equal values of μ. Thus, the parameter μ of the Maxwell-Boltzmann distribution is one-to-one related to the macroscopic quantity temperature; in other words, μ is a function of the temperature. Since a temperature scale represents only a sequence, the parameter μ, or rather $1/\mu$, may be used as a temperature scale. (The relation between this scale—dynamical scale—and the perfect gas temperature scale will be established in the next paragraph.) Thus, we have deduced the macroscopic quantity temperature in terms of the microscopic quantities. Another point may be mentioned here. As the configuration of the composite system changes, the ratio by which the total energy is divided into the two systems also changes. This means that heat flows from one system to the other. Thus, we have also derived the result that the approach of the composite system toward thermal equilibrium is accompanied by the transfer of heat. Since $1/2\mu$ equals the average energy per degree of freedom, the equilibrium condition that the two systems have equal values of μ means that in equilibrium the average energy per degree of freedom is the same for the two interacting systems.

To establish the relation between the dynamical temperature scale defined by $1/\mu$ and the perfect gas temperature scale we need an empirical relation by which the perfect gas temperature is related to the dynamical quantities of the molecules. The perfect gas temperature scale is defined by the equation of state of the perfect gas

$$PV = nRT. \tag{107}$$

We want to express PV in terms of the dynamical quantities of the molecules. This is a purely mechanical problem, since the existence of the pressure, according to the atomic theory, is due to the dynamical action of the molecules (collisions of molecules on the walls). A simple method of finding this relation is as follows: Consider a volume V of perfect gas containing N molecules, the density being N/V. Assume that approximately one-third of the molecules move in the X-direction, one-third in the Y-direction, and one-third in the Z-direction. A unit area on the wall perpendicular to the $+X$ direction will be hit only by those molecules moving in the $+X$ direction, lying in a cylinder with the unit area as base. Within one second there are $(1/6) \times (N/V) \times v$ collisions on the unit area, v being the average velocity of the molecule (this is the number of molecules moving in the $+X$ direction in a cylinder with a height equal v; all of them will collide on the unit area within one second). Each elastic collision causes a transfer of momentum equal to $2mv$ where m is the mass of the molecule. Thus the total momentum transfer per unit area per unit time is the product of $(1/6)(N/V)v$ and $2mv$. Macroscopically, the rate of change of momentum equals the force and the force per unit area is the pressure. Thus

$$P = \frac{1}{6}\frac{N}{V}v \cdot 2mv. \tag{108}$$

In other words,

$$PV = \tfrac{1}{3}Nmv^2$$
$$= \tfrac{2}{3}N(\tfrac{1}{2}mv^2). \tag{109}$$

v (or rather v^2) being averaged over the velocity distribution of a gas, $(1/2)mv^2$ represents the average kinetic energy per molecule. Since a molecule of a perfect gas has three degrees of freedom, the microscopic theory asserts that

$$\tfrac{1}{2}mv^2 = \frac{3}{2\mu} \tag{110}$$

89

The perfect gas temperature scale may now be related to the dynamical scale as follows:

$$nRT = PV = \tfrac{2}{3}N(\tfrac{1}{2}mv^2) = \tfrac{2}{3}N\left(\frac{3}{2}\frac{1}{\mu}\right) = \frac{N}{\mu} \qquad (111)$$

Therefore,

$$\frac{1}{\mu} = \frac{nRT}{N} = kT, \qquad (112)$$

where k is the Boltzmann constant, i.e., the ratio of the universal gas constant and the Avogadro number. Thus the dynamical temperature scale is proportional to the thermodynamic scale; the ratio of the two is the Boltzmann constant. Incidentally, the Maxwell-Boltzmann distribution function may now be written in terms of the perfect gas temperature as follows:

$$N_i = Ae^{-E_i/kT}, \qquad i = 1, 2, \ldots, i, \ldots. \qquad (113)$$

EPILOGUE

METHODOLOGY OF THERMODYNAMICS

The success of modern atomic theory has reduced physics almost entirely to the mechanics of the atom. The laws of mechanics are already known, and we can predict from them the exact mechanical behavior of a system at any future time, once the initial conditions of the system are specified at a particular time. Knowing the physical properties of the atoms, we are able to predict the future behavior of any physical system. The basic problem of a large part of physics is thus solved in principle and no new basic laws are expected to be discovered in this area. For simple mechanical systems, the prediction by mechanical laws may be carried out in great detail for a long period of time. For example, the motion of the planets in the solar system may be predicted very accurately. On the other hand, when the theory is applied to systems of a large number of particles, such as the thermodynamic systems, the exact prediction by the mechanical laws over a long period of time becomes hopelessly complicated. The mechanical laws may still give useful information for a problem involving a short period of time right after the instant at which the initial conditions are specified, but for a problem involving a long period of time, the exact mathematical solution becomes impossible. Yet from the viewpoint of the probability law we can understand the appearance of the equilibrium states. Most systems of a large number of particles reach equilibrium after a certain period of time. The

91

equilibrium state is such that, while the microscopic state keeps on changing according to the laws of mechanics, some macroscopic properties such as pressure and temperature remain unchanged (disregarding fluctuation). This requires that the change of macroscopic property caused by the change of microscopic state of *some* of the molecules must be balanced off by the change caused by *some other* molecules. In a general mechanical state this kind of balancing does not always occur; only in states with special properties may this happen. These special properties are characteristic of equilibrium states. From the condition of exact balancing we may hope to deduce these special features (physical and chemical properties) of the equilibrium states. Therefore beyond the laws of mechanics, we have found another source of physical information—the equilibrium conditions. Heretofore, the laws of mechanics have been the sole source of physical information. The achievement of statistical mechanics demonstrates the reward of the exploitation of this new source in the microscopic theory. In the macroscopic theory when we find problems beyond mechanics (heat phenomena) the only other source of physical information we can turn to is the macroscopic equilibrium conditions. Therefore, we have developed thermodynamics here starting from a discussion of the macroscopic equilibrium. The ensuing developments, such as the determination of the change of entropy in the adiabatic, isothermal, and diffusive reversible processes, are based on the application of the equilibrium conditions to a few special physical processes. Thus from the methodological point of view our approach seems the most direct, most physical approach, not just the re-weaving of old threads in a new pattern. The shortcomings of the earlier formulations originate from the fact that they do not start from the basic source of physical information, but try to work into it from some other standpoint. As a result, logical difficulties appear and the theory is left in an incomplete state. The ingenuity by which classical thermodynamics is established by way of engineering is one of the marvels in the history of science, but its significance is essentially historical.

INDEX